*Evolutionary
Ecology*

Contemporary Thought in Ecological Science Series

Arthur S. Boughey/Editor

Lowell Adams	Population Ecology
Peter H. Klopfer	Behavioral Ecology
Herbert P. Riley	Evolutionary Ecology

Dickenson Series in Biology

Elof Axel Carlson/Consulting Editor

Donald J. Reish	Biology of the Oceans
Kenneth E. Maxwell	Chemicals and Life
Arthur S. Boughey	Contemporary Readings in Ecology

Contemporary Thought in Biological Science Series

Elof Axel Carlson/Consulting Editor

Bruce H. Carpenter	Molecular and Cell Biology
Edward Glassman	Molecular Approaches to Psychobiology
Elof A. Carlson	Gene Theory
J. Richard Whittaker	Cellular Differentiation
Arthur S. Boughey	Population and Environmental Biology
J. Eugene Fox	Molecular Control of Plant Growth
Rodolfo Ruibal	The Adaptations of Organisms

Herbert P. Riley / *Evolutionary*

UNIVERSITY OF CALIFORNIA, IRVINE

Ecology

Dickenson Publishing Company, Inc., Belmont, California

575
R 45 e
74275
April, 1971

Library of Congress Catalog Card Number:
72-103042
Printed in the United States of America

1 2 3 4 5 6 7 8 9 10—73 72 71 70

Contents

Foreword

The science of ecology has vital implications for the many urgent problems which now beset us. Yet there is a dearth of readily accessible ecological information. While the ecosystem approach has provided a new direction and a new unity to the discipline, published information on the various aspects of ecology is still widely scattered through a great range of scientific publications.

Each volume in the series on CONTEMPORARY THOUGHT IN ECOLOGICAL SCIENCE gathers relevant material which presents current progress and contemporary ideas in some particular field of ecology. The various selections are carefully chosen to present to the teacher and student alike a deeper insight into both the problems and conclusions of recent research. Each collection of readings illustrates the direction of investigations and the modern concepts within the major interrelated fields which comprise the science of ecology.

The readings are intended for use in upper division and graduate courses in ecology. Collectively the series demonstrates the essential unity of modern ecology and establishes the fact that it is not an isolated discipline, but extends into all aspects of biology. Individual readings also illustrate the creative manner in which ecological advances are achieved and provide examples of how independent observations come to be incorporated in general concepts. The range of readings material emphasizes the growing realization that if we are to survive on this planet, our approach in the next millennium will have to be based on established ecological principles.

Arthur S. Boughey
Series Editor

Preface

This small book comprises readings on the nature of variation, natural selection, ecological adaptation, and ecological evolution. The problem of *variation* is a fundamental one for the study of evolution, because without variation there could be no evolution. Darwin's and Wallace's main contribution to evolutionary theory was the theory of *natural selection* as the agent of evolutionary change. Natural selection is brought about by a reaction between the phenotype and the environment and operates on variations that either exist or might arise because of the nature of the genotype. If a new phenotype arises as the result of genotypic changes, it may be better or worse suited to life in a particular environment, or, as it is usually expressed, better or worse *adapted* to that environment. If it is better adapted, it will be preserved; if it is worse adapted, it will tend to be eliminated. New phenotypes may sometimes arise through hybridization between species. There are many definitions of the term *species*, and a consideration of them is beyond the scope of this book. Biologically, a species can be considered to be a group of similar individuals that typically breed true, that breed, or at least can breed, with one another, and that do not successfully interbreed with individuals of other species under natural conditions. The ecological factors that often keep species from coming together to hybridize and that sometimes prevent the hybrids from surviving and becoming established are important considerations for the study of evolution in any group of plants and animals.

The age-old question of heredity and environment—nature and nurture—is being restated today in new terms. We are realizing more and more that the only variation that is relevant to evolution is inherited variation, but variants are preserved or lost according to the environment in which they live. Thus the environment affects heredity not by changing the genotype through the inheritance of acquired characteristics, as was once believed, but by selecting for survival and, what is more important, for reproduction, those variants that are adapted to that environment. Thus, if Lamarck's short-necked primitive giraffe had decided to be the progenitor of a race of long-necked creatures, he probably did so not, as Lamarck assumed, by continuing to stretch his neck (which might eventually have been painful to him), but by moving to an environment to which only his longer-necked progeny would be adapted and by instructing those long-necked offspring that survived to do likewise and to pass the word along to a number of future generations. Thus, by continued selection, only certain genotypes would be perpetuated.

The significance of Darwin's contribution was minimized during the first two or three decades of the twentieth century because of the rise of classical genetics and emphasis on the mutation theory. The recent development of the field of population genetics and the realization that natural selection is concerned with populations rather than with individuals have revived interest in Darwin's views.

These readings include some contemporary studies of topics involved in a consideration of evolution and its ecological aspects. The papers selected were published between 1963 and 1968 in a number of different journals. Many more could have been included had space permitted. An attempt was made to choose studies of a wide variety of organisms and environments and to show some current trends in the field. Most of the papers include bibliographies that might well be consulted for further reading. The papers have been grouped into four chapters, and a brief commentary introduces each chapter. The chapters are: Nature of Variation, Natural Selection, Ecological Adaptation, and Ecological Evolution.

Irvine, California   HERBERT PARKES RILEY

Evolutionary
Ecology

1 / Nature of Variation

Inherited types of variation include gene mutations, chromosome mutation or aberrations, and gene recombination. Chromosome aberrations have been studied intensively since the late 1920's in plants and since 1956 in human beings and other mammals. These aberrations involve whole chromosomes (aneuploids), whole sets of chromosomes (*polyploids* or *euploids*), or parts of one or more chromosomes.

Chromosomal evolution sometimes involves a series of different basic chromosome numbers. Lewis, Oliver, and Suda describe such a series in *Claytonia virginica*, including plants with base numbers of 6, 7, and 8. Polyloids with high chromosome numbers are described by Bose and Flory. In *Sprekelia formosissima*, the original diploids have apparently died out; in the course of evolution, chromosomal aberrations occurred and modified the original karyotype.

To compare chromosomes of related organisms, *karyotypes* showing the size and shape of each chromosome and the location of the centromeres, secondary constrictions, and satellites are often used. Hsu, Reardon, and Luquette show that the karyotypes of nine species of the Felidae are remarkably similar, with most of the chromosomes metacentric.

Lethal "genes" are often actually chromosome deletions or deficiencies. D. L. Jennings, the Scottish geneticist, shows that in *Rubus* polymorphism and heterozygosity can be maintained in a population by a balanced lethal system.

Cytogeography of *Claytonia virginica* and Its Allies

Walter H. Lewis

Royce L. Oliver

Yutaka Suda

Abstract

On the basis of chromosome numbers from more than 1,000 individuals of *Claytonia virginica* L. (*Portulacaceae*) throughout its range, a complex evolution of major cytotypes is discussed in relation to distribution and morphology. Chromosomal diversity is thought to have evolved from a base of $n = 6$ by hyperaneuploidy to $n = 7$ and 8 with each race giving rise to widespread and dominant primary tetraploids ($n = 12, 14, 16$). These in turn, and largely by hypoaneuploidy, formed many secondary tetraploid races, the most significant of which are $n = 11$ and 15. Higher polyploids from $6x$ to $12x$ where $x = 6$, and $6x$ and $8x$ where $x = 7$ are also discussed. Infraspecific phylogeny is compared with data for two allied species, *C. caroliniana* Michx. and *C. lanceolata* Pursh, which show striking parallels with *C. virginica* in chromosomal evolution. By one morphological character, leaf width, the cytotypes separate into two groups, not along diploid vs. polypoid lines, but rather a narrow-leafed var. *acutiflora* DC. with $n = 6, 7, 12\pm$, and $14\pm$ and a broad-leafed var. *virginica* with $n = 8$ and $16\pm$.

From collections made throughout eastern North America over 1,000 plants of *Claytonia virginica* L. (*Portulacaceae*) have been examined chromosomally. With the exception of Rothwell (1959) earlier studies have been limited in scope although all have made a substantial contribution to a cytogeographic understanding of the species (Bell, 1965; Davis & Bowmer, 1966; Lewis, 1959, 1962, 1967; Lewis et al., 1962, 1967; Rothwell & Kump, 1965). While these studies illustrated a wide diversity of chromosome number for *C. virginica* ($2n = 12$ to ca 191) none was extensive enough to indicate total distribution of all major cytotypes; rather only for a few from very limited areas, viz. dominance of $x = 7$ in eastern Texas (Lewis, 1962), $x = 8$ in Indiana (Rothwell, 1959), and $n = 12$ and 15 in the St. Louis, Missouri area (Lewis et al., 1967). We shall attempt with our additional data to present the distribution of cytotypes occurring in the eastern half of the continent and to suggest their probable evolution. Cytogeography and evolution of *C. virginica* will be compared with several allied species as well as briefly with the primitive species of *Claytonia*. In addition gross morphological diversity will be correlated with the various cytotypes and discussed in relation to distribution.

• • •

Reprinted by permission of the authors and publisher from *Annals of the Missouri Botanical Garden* **54**: 153–171, 1967.

Cytology

Before proceeding with a discussion of major cytotypes two phenomena will be noted briefly. These include aneusomaty, i.e. variation of chromosome number intra-individually, which was found by Lewis et al. (1967) in the St. Louis area and earlier in eastern Texas (Lewis, 1962). No additional data can be added to this phenomenon. We wish also to mention the results of Rothwell & Kump (1965) from the New York area in which they reported highly polyploid individuals ($2n = 85$ to ca 191) occasionally associated with meiotically regular diploids ($2n = 16$). Such individuals have not been found elsewhere, but their diversity in New York (perhaps formed in response to some local environmental circumstance, e.g. viruses) does illustrate a propensity for mass chromosomal duplication without apparent harm to the individual.

Elsewhere the results are more orderly. Of the three major diploid cytotypes (Fig. 1), that having $n = 6$ is restricted to the geologically old and well-known relict and refugial area in the southern Appalachian Mountains. Here, found in mixed and separate populations, are plants with $n = 7$. This race is also found in the geologically similar Ozarks and to the south of these mountains as a common weed almost to the Gulf of Mexico. The $n = 7$ race is now disjunct, but very probably had a common origin and was continuous much earlier. The third major diploid race is based on 8; it dominates the northern distribution of *C. virginica* and has by far the greatest continuous range of any diploid. To the south, its limits parallel somewhat the southern expansion of the last glaciation (Fig. 1). Rarely individuals with $n = 8$ occur outside this area, e.g. in eastern Texas, but they probably represent spontaneous, local aneuploids quite apart from the major trends of evolution.

Other diploid cytotypes are known, but these are rare and none has a distinct distribution. The $n = 9$ race, for example, is found very rarely in eastern Texas in populations dominated by plants with $n = 7$ and where $n = 8$ is rare in a declining frequency from $n = 7$-8-9 with only one plant having $2n = 15$. Paralleling this Rothwell (1959) reported in a single population 73 plants with $n = 8$, 13 with $n = 9$, and 3 with $n = 10$ as well as aneuploids with $8_{II} + 1_I$ and $9_{II} + 1_I$. From only two plants of an Ontario population (*Lewis 6630*) we found one plant with $n = 8$ and one with $n = 9$. Although it cannot be excluded that a race dominated by plants having $n = 9$ may yet be found in the northern range of *C. virginica*, where counts are as yet meagre, autodiploids other than $n = 6$, 7, and 8 are infrequent and sporadic and probably arose by chromosomal gain through meiotic non-disjunction over and over again locally from plants representing the dominant diploid for the area.

The primary tetraploid cytotypes of each of the major diploid races ($n = 12$, 14, 16) are very common and have widespread overlapping distributions. . . . All major tetraploids may be found together, but invariably one or two races

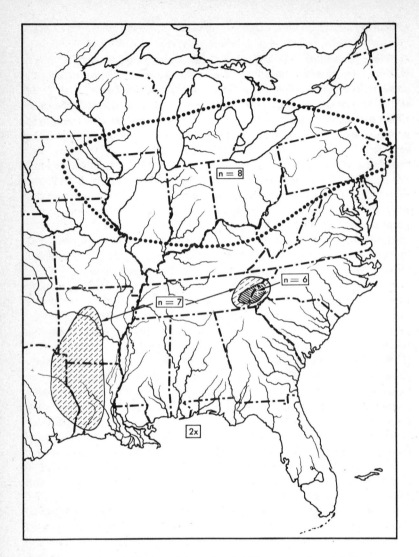

Fig. 1. Distribution of the major diploid cytotypes ($n = 6, 7, 8$)
of *Claytonia virginica* in eastern North America.

dominate at any one locality. For example in the St. Louis area, where
diploids are unknown, two tetraploid races are dominant and more or less
of equal frequency; they usually are found at distinct localities even in this
small area although both races are occasionally found together.

Secondary tetraploid races are also frequent, but usually in association with primary tetraploid cytotypes from which they probably arose. In the St. Louis area $n = 15$ is much more common than $n = 16$, but at several localities both occur in addition to $15_{II} + 1_I$. Elsewhere particularly in the Midwest this pattern is repeated or reversed, i.e. dominance of $n = 16$ with fewer secondary tetraploids. . . . Widespread also are plants with $n = 11$; these are secondary tetraploids probably formed by hypoaneuploidy from those with $n = 12$ with which they are usually associated. Sporadically throughout the range of *C. virginica* other secondary tetraploids are found, but none is frequent.

Of the higher polyploid races only those with $n = 18$, presumably hexaploids in the $x = 6$ line, are frequent and widespread; less common are those with $n = 24$ ($8x$) and 36 ($12x$) based on 6. More infrequent still are those with $n = 21$ ($6x$) and 28 ($8x$) where $x = 7$.

The $x = 6$ line has the greatest range and is the most highly polyploid; as already noted the $2x$ is restricted to the southern Appalachians and the $4x$ is widely distributed; the $6x$ is less frequent but found within the range of the tetraploid; the $8x$ is rare though similar to the hexaploid in distribution; and the $12x$ is also rare but more restricted (mid-Atlantic states and mid-Appalachians).

For the $x = 7$ race we have noted the disjunct distribution of the southern $2x$ as well as the wide range of the $4x$ race. The $6x$ and $8x$ races are very rare and local.

Only two races are clearly based on 8. The diploid is northern, the tetraploid extends more to the south and both are of wide range. No octoploid, $n = 32$, is known.

Comparative frequency for all significant cytotypes is presented in Fig. 2; a rough index at best because sampling has been better in some areas than in others. Yet the diagram does accurately reflect, we believe, an increase in frequency among the diploid races from $n = 6$ to 8 with an abrupt decrease to $n = 9$ and 10 (representatives of the latter race may have evolved by chromosomal loss from tetraploids or by hyperaneuploidy from diploids). This sequence suggests hyperaneuploidy from $n = 6$, a very old and apparently relict race for *C. virginica* and one which may be basic for the genus if not the family. Perhaps also the antiquity of this basic number is reflected by the extensive polyploid series from $n = 6$, far greater than for any other basic line.

Judging from Fig. 2, however, *C. virginica* is dominated by plants at the tetraploid level. They presumably evolved along at least three distinct lines from $n = 6$ to 12, $n = 7$ to 14, and $n = 8$ to 16, perhaps through unreduced gametes. The first successful mutation was probably from $n = 6$ to 12, the former now very restricted, the latter now forming one of the largest and most frequent cytotypes in the species. They are not known to be sympatric although our data are meagre from the mid-Appalachian region where

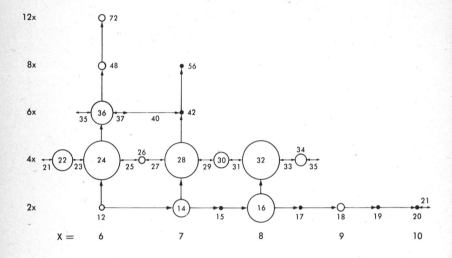

Fig. 2. Comparative frequency of cytotypes (as $2n$) in *Claytonia virginica* and suggested evolutionary direction. The smallest circle represents the occurrence of a race in one population, others to scale.

they might occur together. Cytotypes of the other lines, however, are often found at the same locality, e.g. $n = 7$ and 14 in eastern Texas, $n = 8$ and 16 in Indiana.

A significant feature of tetraploids is the frequency of their secondary races, particularly $n = 11$ and 15 (Fig. 2). Their origins from $n = 12$ and 16, respectively, have already been noted. Other such tetraploids are known and these in total account for a large fraction of individuals examined. Clearly chromosomal change at the tetraploid level has been much greater than at the diploid level; presumably this redundancy of chromosomes has allowed a greater shift in complements without deleterious effects. Moreover change among tetraploids appears strongly downward (hypoaneutetraploidy) in contrast to the diploid level where chromosomal gain has apparently been more important (hyperaneudiploidy).

Probably through unreduced gametes or less likely by doubling of $2x$-$4x$ crosses (no definite triploid has yet been found) or by both, the higher polyploids evolved. Their frequency and direction of evolution are suggested in Fig. 2.

• • •

Literature Cited

Bell, C. R. 1965. *In* Documented plant chromosome numbers. *Sida* **2**: 168–170.

Davis, R. J. 1966. The North American perennial species of *Claytonia*. *Brittonia* **18**: 285–303.

———— and R. G. Bowmer. 1966. Chromosome numbers in *Claytonia*. *Brittonia* **18**: 37–38.

Gleason, H. A. and A. Cronquist. 1963. Manual of vascular plants of northeastern United States and adjacent Canada. D. v. Nostrand Co., Princeton.

Lewis, W. H. 1959. Three chromosome numbers for *Claytonia* (*Portulacaceae*). *Southwest. Nat.* **3**: 130–132.

————. 1962. Aneusomaty in aneuploid populations of *Claytonia virginica*. *Amer. Jour. Bot.* **49**: 918–928.

————. 1967. Cytocatalytic evolution in plants. *Bot. Rev.* **33**: 105–115.

————, H. L. Stripling and R. G. Ross. 1962. Chromosome numbers for some angiosperms of the southern United States and Mexico. *Rhodora* **64**: 147–161.

————, Y. Suda and B. MacBryde. 1967. Chromosome numbers of *Claytonia virginica* in the St. Louis, Missouri area. *Ann. Missouri Bot. Gard.* **54**: 147–152.

Rothwell, N. V. 1959. Aneuploidy in *Claytonia virginica*. *Amer. Jour. Bot.* **46**: 353–360.

———— and J. G. Kump. 1965. Chromosome numbers in populations of *Claytonia virginica* from the New York metropolitan area. *Amer. Jour. Bot.* **52**: 403–407.

Swanson, J. R. 1966. A synopsis of relationships in *Montioideae* (*Portulacaceae*). *Brittonia* **18**: 229–241.

Taylor, R. L. and R. P. Brockman. 1966. Chromosome numbers of some western Canadian plants. *Canad. Jour. Bot.* **44**: 1093–1103.

A Cytological Study of *Sprekelia formosissima* Herbert

Smritimoy Bose

W. S. Flory

Sprekelia is a monotypic genus of the Amaryllidaceae, native to Mexico and Guatemala. In Mexico reports of its occurrence in the states of Chihuahua, Durango, Guerrero, Hidalgo, Jalisco, Mexico, Morelos and Michoacan are available. *Sprekelia formosissima* Herbert is a species of comparatively slight variation. There are occasional plants having flowers with some colour variation, or with leaves that are glaucous in varying degrees. Several such forms were described by Baker (1888), and there are more recent reports in the literature of similar taxa. Perhaps a more pronounced variation is in flower size, although the distinctions here seem to be overlooked more readily.

Several persons have reported chromosome numbers in *Sprekelia formosissima*. Somatic numbers have been reported of approximately 110 by Inariyama (1937), of from 110 to 117 by Sato (1938), of about 121 by Snoad (1952), and of 116 by Mookerjea (1955). Bose (1958) has published a preliminary report on a part of the present work.

Because of the variable, and perhaps uncertain, chromosome numbers reported it seemed desirable to study the chromosomes of *Sprekelia* in some detail in connection with a more extensive cytological study of the Amaryllidaceae. It also seemed desirable to take into account the variable size of flowers of different plants in making the study.

· · ·

Discussion

Chromosome Number in *Sprekelia*

The five bulbs of *S. formosissima* from Cuernavaca have a somatic chromosome number of 60. Only occasionally have numbers of 58, 59 or 61 been encountered in cells of these plants.

Bulbs of the species which were secured from commercial houses have about 120 chromosomes, although out of 12 unbroken cells in which the exact number was determined the actual number of 120 occurred in only two cells. In six cells the number was more, in 4 cells less, than 120. Likewise in the bulb with about 150 chromosomes, an actual 150 occurred only twice, while slightly higher numbers were found in two cells, and slightly lower numbers three times out of seven unbroken cells with numbers definitely determined. In thirteen unbroken cells, numbers were definitely determined which were well

Reprinted by permission of the authors and publisher from *The Nucleus* **8**: 115–128, 1965.

above the 150 range. These numbers ranged from 164 to 178. None of these quite reached the number of 180, although these thirteen numbers are the ones which we have designated as about 180.

TABLE 1

Numbers of chromosomes of each of the different types encountered in the different chromosome number races of *Sprekelia formosissima* Herbert

Chromosome types	Numbers of the several types in different 2n races			
	60	ca. 120	ca. 150	ca. 180
A	2	4	5	5–6
B_1	4	8	10	12
B_2	8	16	20	24
C_1	6	12	15	18
C_2	6	12	15	18
C_3	8	16	20	24
C_4	8	16	20	24
C_5	8	16	20	24
C_6	8	16	20	24
D	2	3–(4)	3–(5)	4–(6)

It was suspected that *Sprekelia formosissima* forms with 2n = 30 may exist in native localities. With this view the junior author (in company with Dr. R. O. Flagg, and Mr. and Mrs. M. W. Clint) in 1961 made collections of the species at a number of native habitats in Mexico. In these collections special effort was made to secure bulbs producing smaller flowers, or flowers with narrower perianth segments. Not all of the 1961 collections have been cytologically analyzed as yet, but of the more likely ones studied no numbers of less than 2n = 60 have been encountered.

Chromosome numbers have earlier been reported for *Sprekelia* as 110, as 110 to 117, as 121, and as 116, by Inariyama (1937), Sato (1938), Snoad (1952) and Mookerjea (1955), respectively. All of these counts were apparently made on material comparable to bulbs of the present investigation derived from commercial sources, where 2n = about 120, but with several definite numbers both below and above 120 being observed. The numbers observed by these earlier workers are quite in line with the present observations. When put into perspective with cytological observations presented here on this same general chromosome race, along with taxa of the species with higher and with lower chromosome numbers, a more plausible picture of the true situation becomes apparent.

It appears that in *Sprekelia* there is a euploid series in which known chromosome numbers of 60, 120, 150 and about 180 occur. There may be plants with additional chromosome numbers, not yet encountered, in the series. Cells with aneuploid numbers have been found in plants having all these euploid numbers, with such aneuploid cells being quite frequent in plants with the higher chromosome numbers.

The chromosomes of *Sprekelia* range up to over 12 micra in length, following colchicine treatment. It is true that some chromosomes are quite short. With 2n = 60, however, there is a total chromosome length of about 363 micra, or an average of just over 6 micra per chromosome. This means that at somatic metaphase the cells are quite crowded with chromosomes, and the crowding situation is aggravated with increasing numbers of chromosomes.

The ca. 120, ca. 150 and ca. 180 chromosome races range between 118–124, 148–155, and 164–178 chromosomes, respectively for the cells counted. It is likely that the increase in chromosomes to these high numbers would in itself decrease mitotic efficiency because of crowding, or some other disturbance of nuclear balance. This could plausibly account for higher than expected numbers of chromosomes entering some cells, with lesser numbers going to sister cells. It could explain the number of cells with more or less than 120, 150, or 180 chromosomes in the *Sprekelia* euploid series. Such chromosome crowding caused by increase of chromosome number was suggested by Menzel and Brown (1952) as a probable cause for the varying chromosome numbers associated with mosaic formation in their hexaploid (2n = 78) *Gossypium* hybrids. With considerably higher numbers of chromosomes, in most of the present accessions, such crowding would seem an even more likely cause of uneven division resulting in cells with aneuploid numbers.

Basic Chromosome Number in *Sprekelia*

With a euploid series of 60, ca. 120, ca. 150 and ca. 180 chromosomes being known, a base number of 30 chromosomes for *Sprekelia* occurs, of course, as a strong possibility. If this is the case, then taxa which are essentially diploid, tetraploid, pentaploid and hexaploid have been dealt with. Actually, in counts with races having more than 60 chromosomes, cells which are aneuploid deviates are more frequent than are those with exact multiples of 30 chromosomes. The numbers of each different type of chromosome observed (Table 1) would seem to substantiate the reasoning that 30 is a base number; only 2 chromosomes of type A, 2 chromosomes of type D, and 4 chromosomes of type B have been observed with 2n = 60, with similar representation of these types in the races with higher numbers.

It is conceivable, and perhaps more logical, to think that a basic number of n = 30 was derived, at least, from a lower base number. The most recent arrangement of the genera of Amaryllidaceae (Traub, 1963) places *Sprekelia* in tribe Zephyrantheae. In this tribe *Habranthus, Cooperia, Zephyranthes*, and perhaps other genera, quite obviously have 6 as a basic chromosome number (Flory, 1958). It seems reasonable to suspect that the basic chromosome number in *Sprekelia* also is 6, rather than 30. If 6 is the base number in *Sprekelia*, it would mean that in the process of karyotype evolution, translocations or other cytological changes have occurred, since the chromosome types now encountered in *Sprekelia* (Table 1) are not present in the proper numbers to satisfy this conception, otherwise. It is of probable significance that *Sprekelia* occurs in an area where *Zephyranthes* is represented by a number of species, and where *Cooperia* and *Habranthus* are also prevalent.

• • •

References

Baker, J. G. 1888. *Handbook of the Amaryllidaceae*. George Bell and Sons. London. 216 pp.

Bose, S. 1958. Cytological studies in parental types, and in selfed and crossed progenies of *Sprekelia formosissima* Herbert. *Proc. X Int. Genetics Congress* **2**: 30–31.

Flory, W. S., Jr. 1958. Speciation, mitotic chromosome number, and karyotype evolution in the Amaryllidaceae. *Proc. X Int. Genetics Congress* **2**: 82.

Inariyama, S. 1937. Karyotype studies in Amaryllidaceae. I. Sci. Rep. Tokyo. *Burnika Daigaku* Ser. No. **52**: 95–113.

Menzel, M. Y. and M. S. Brown, 1952. Polygenomic hybrids in *Gossypium*. II. Mosaic formation and somatic reduction. *Amer. Jour. Bot.* **39**: 59–69.

Mookerjea, A. 1955. Cytology of Amaryllids as an aid to the understanding of evolution *Caryologia* **7**: 1–71.

Sato, D. 1938. Karyotype alteration and phylogeny. IV. Karyotypes in Amaryllidaceae with special reference to the Sat-chromosomes. *Cytologia* **9**: 203–242.

Snoad, B. 1955. (In C. D. Darlington and A. P. Wylie's "Chromosome Atlas of Flowering Plants," p. 383).

Traub, H. P. 1963. The Genera of Amaryllidaceae. *Amer. Pl. Life Soc.* La Jolla, Calif. 85 pp.

Karyological Studies of Nine Species of Felidae

T. C. Hsu

Helen H. Rearden

George F. Luquette

Cytological research has made a considerable contribution to the study of evolution. In Dipterous insects, the giant chromosomes in the salivary glands have helped to reveal sequences of structural changes occurring in chromosomes by which the divergence of species can be traced from interspecific and interracial hybrids (Patterson and Stone, 1952).

In some groups of plants and animals, when crossing between species is feasible, information concerning genetic relationships can be obtained from the chromosome behavior during meiosis. When interspecific crosses are not feasible, less precise information can be obtained by karyotypic analysis from mitotic metaphases. However, such work has been exceedingly deficient in the class Mammalia. The impediment of this line of research is based primarily on technical limitations. Before the newer technical innovations inaugurated during the 50's, karyology of mammals, including man, was one of the most poorly developed fields in cytology. Using classical sectioning procedure, or the squash method without pretreatment, even determining the diploid number of a species was a difficult task (as exemplified by the study of man), quite aside from morphological characterization of the entire chromosome complement. After examining countless references in the literature, Matthey (1958) listed only 241 Eutherian species whose diploid number was considered by him to be correct. Among these, many were obtained from meiotic metaphase at which stage chromosome morphology hardly can be used for effective comparison, and many were determined in recent years.

Several methodological improvements have opened a new horizon for mammalian karyology: (1) the application of tissue culture techniques to cytology, providing the investigators with ample supplies of cells in mitosis, (2) the use of hypotonic solution pretreatment to spread the chromosomes, (3) the employment of colchicine to contract the chromosomes, and (4) the application of squash methods or methods of air drying to force the chromosomes into one plane of focus. Thus, many problems in karyology can be tackled with a precision undreamed of by cytologists two decades ago.

With these improvements, much attention has been paid during recent years to human cytogenetics and cancer cytology, but with the exception of

Reprinted by permission of the authors and The University of Chicago Press from *The American Naturalist* **97**: 225–234, 1963. © 1963 by the University of Chicago. All rights reserved. Published 1963.

studies on primates (Chu and Bender, 1961) no corresponding emphasis has been placed on phylogenetic studies. Idiograms are limited to only a few domestic animals, and to some laboratory animals.

In our opinion, with the exception of a few recent investigations, the chromosomes of practically all mammalian species should be reinvestigated to provide more meaningful data for phylogenetic studies. In this communication we present examples to demonstrate that a wealth of materials, kept in many zoological gardens, could be utilized to advantage.

• • •

Results

Makino and Tateishi (1952) described the chromosomes of three species of Felidae: the domestic cat (*Felis domestica*), the lion (*F. leo*) and the Chinese leopard (*F. bengalensis*). According to these authors, the diploid number of all three species is 38. They also stated that the chromosome morphology is similar from one species to another, but unfortunately their idiograms, not being made with modern techniques, are not legible.

With the exception of the jaguarundi culture, all grew well to provide ample mitotic cells for detailed analysis. The cultures of the jaguarundi showed few mitoses. However, a correct count was made on three cells and the diploid number of this species is as that of the majority of members in this family, 38. Two species, *F. pardalis* and *F. wiedii*, have a diploid number of 36.

It is true that there is a striking similarity among the karyotypes of individual species of this family so far examined, including the domestic cat studied by M. S. Sasaki (personal communication). According to size and morphology, the chromosomes can be classified into eight groups. Since variation in number of chromosome pairs occurs in certain groups from species to species, merely assigning a numeral to each pair may confuse reference. We hereby suggest the use of both the group and numeral symbols for nomenclature, so that seemingly homologous chromosomes among species can bear the same label. Thus, chromosome B1 of one species corresponds to chromosome B1 of another, etc.

Group A. Large subtelocentrics; four or five pairs, including one pair of large submetacentrics. The large submetacentric (No. A1) is the largest pair of the entire complement. Its long arm is approximately twice as long as the short arm. Every species possesses this pair which can be identified unequivocally in practically all metaphase figures. The second largest pair of this group (A2) is also present in every species and is very easy to identify. Its long arm is approximately four times as long as the short arm. Other chromosomes of this group are comparatively smaller than the first two and are similar in size and in arm ratio. Three species (puma, ocelot, and marguay) possess three such pairs, but the rest of the species have only two.

Group B. Large or medium metacentrics; three or four pairs, including the X chromosome. The largest of this group, B1, is the second largest pair of each complement. It is very easy to identify, and is present in every karyotype. The X chromosome is medium-sized and is slightly unequal in arm ratio. However, in the idiogram of the domestic cat constructed by Sasaki, the X chromosomes are a pair of small-sized metacentrics.

Group C. Medium submetacentrics, one to three pairs. Generally one pair (C1) is of fairly large size, which in most cases can be identified without too much difficulty. In the puma, this is the only pair that can be classified into Group C. Other pairs are difficult to distinguish, and in cells with more contracted chromosomes it is sometimes not easy to determine whether a pair belongs to Group B or Group C.

Group D. Small submetacentrics and subtelocentrics; four or five pairs. They are not easy to distinguish and the numeral designations should not be used for determination of homology. In the idiograms of the ocelot and the marguay, a pair of subtelocentrics (D4) is prominent. It is not known that the D4 pair in the idiogram of the lion corresponds to D4 of the ocelot. In other species this pair cannot be clearly identified.

Group E. Small subtelocentrics with conspicuous satellite; one pair (E1). This pair can be identified unequivocally in every species and practically in every cell.

Group F. Small metacentrics; two or three pairs. In species with two pairs, one (F1) is always larger than the other (F2). In those with three pairs (puma and cheetah), two larger pairs are present. However, the second larger pair (F3) is more or less submetacentric.

Group G. Small telocentrics; maximum two pairs. In the ocelot and marguay, no such chromosomes can be found. Identification of individual members within this group is very difficult.

Group H. The Y chromosome. The Y is naturally absent in females. It is a small subtelocentric, generally more pyknotic in appearance than are other chromosomes, except in the ocelot, where it is exceedingly small and does not appear heteropyknotic. The short arm varies in length, but identification of the Y is not difficult.

Discussion

It is obvious from the nine karyotypes studied in this article, and from that of the domestic cat analyzed by other investigators, that the family Felidae is a cytologically homogeneous group. Although there is no direct evidence to prove, for example, that chromosome A1 of one species is strictly homologous to the apparently corresponding chromosome of another, morphological characteristics of many such elements, especially those of pair E1, suggest homology.

In many groups of animals, the Robertsonian effect, namely, two telocentric chromosomes forming a metacentric, appears to play a role in speciation. Thus as species are more and more evolved, more and more metacentrics can be observed in the karyotype. The cats appear to have passed the earlier stage because most chromosomes are already biarmed. Judged by available data, the highest diploid number of telocentrics is four (*Panthera onca, P. pardus* and *Lynx rufus*). Thus, there will be a chance for the formation of one more pair of metacentrics in these species. The fact that the ocelot and the marguay possess an extra pair of medium metacentrics (B3?) but no telocentrics is strongly suggestive of the probable fate of telocentrics.

The change in chromosome morphology observed in some cases, therefore, is presumably accomplished by pericentric inversions, deletions, and reciprocal translocations. The presence of three pairs of small metacentrics in *F. concolor* and in *Acinonyx jabatus*, concomitant with the elimination of one pair of small telocentrics, suggests a pericentric inversion. Most likely, it is the F3 pair. However, in the case of the lion, the absence of one of the G pairs is not accompanied by the appearance of an added F pair, but by a D pair. The D4 pair, consisting of subtelocentrics with very small second arms, could be classified by some cytologists into the G group. However, eight idiograms analyzed unequivocally compel agreement that the small second arm exists.

In spite of the morphological and cytological similarities between the ocelot and the marguay, these two species differ in one karyological characteristic, viz., the size of the Y chromosome. The Y of the marguay is not especially different from that of other species, but that of the ocelot is extremely small, one of the smallest Y chromosomes ever observed in animals. Since no chromosome pair in the ocelot is significantly larger than the corresponding pair in the marguay in a manner that would suggest a process of reciprocal translocation, indication is strong that a deletion has taken place during the formation of the Y. It is interesting to point out that genetically the Y chromosome is considered largely inert. Thus, a partial loss of an inert piece would not affect the survival of the bearer.

The number of species analyzed is far from sufficient to warrant speculation concerning the relationships among members of Felidae and the trend of evolution within the family. Perhaps studies on some more primitive forms will throw light on the origin of the metacentrics. It is, however, surprising to see that the karyotype of *Acinonyx jabatus*, a species quite different morphologically from the rest of the cats, is strictly feline without particular deviations.

A recent article on the chromosome analysis of North American chipmunks (Nadler and Block, 1962) also shows the karyological similarity of species; *Tamias* and *Eutamias* form a relatively homogeneous group. Nadler and Block used bone marrow *in situ* as their material. When animals can be sacrificed, this technique is perhaps effective; but with large and expensive animals, cultivation of biopsy specimens is still the most reasonable method.

Summary

The somatic metaphase chromosomes of nine species of Felidae were analyzed from cells grown in tissue culture initiated with small skin biopsies. Seven species show a diploid chromosome number of 38, and the remaining two, 36. There are remarkable similarities among the karyotypes so far studied.

Literature Cited

Chu, E. H. Y., and M. A. Bender, 1961, Chromosome cytology and evolution in primates. *Science* **133**: 1399–1405.

Hsu, T. C., and D. S. Kellogg, 1960, Primary cultivation and continuous propagation of cells *in vitro* from small biopsy specimens. *J. Natl. Cancer Inst.* **25**: 211–235.

Makino, S., and S. Tateishi, 1952, A comparison of the chromosomes in the lion, Chinese leopard cat and house cat. *J. Morphol.* **90**: 93–102.

Matthey, R., 1958, Les chromosomes des mammiferes eutherians liste critique et essai sur l'evolution chromosomique. Arch. Julius Klaus-Stift. Vererbungsforsch. Sozialanthropol. *Rassenhyg.* **33**: 253–297.

Moorhead, P. S., P. C. Nowell, W. J. Mellman, D. M. Battips, and D. A. Hungerford, 1960, Chromosome preparations of leukocytes cultured from human peripheral blood. *Exp. Cell Res.* **20**: 613–616.

Nadler, C. F., and M. H. Block, 1962, The chromosomes of some North American chipmunks (*Sciuridae*) belonging to the genera *Tamias* and *Eutamias*. *Chromosoma* **13**: 1–15.

Patterson, J. T., and W. S. Stone, 1952, *Evolution in the Genus Drosophila.* Macmillan, New York.

Balanced Lethals and Polymorphism in
Rubus idaeus

D. L. Jennings

Introduction

Several writers (Grubb, 1922; Lewis, 1939; Jennings, 1964) have commented upon the high frequency with which colonies of *Rubus idaeus* are polymorphic for glabrous and sub-glabrous plants, and though there is less evidence for polymorphism in respect of pigmented and non-pigmented plants, there is evidence that many populations maintain high frequencies of alternative alleles of the gene which determines this difference. These observations on natural populations of *Rubus idaeus* are supported by data from experimental progenies of wild raspberries, and by the results of breeding experiments on certain cultivars believed to be closely related to wild populations (Jennings, 1963). There are two gene loci involved in the inheritance of these differences—the $H:h$ locus, which determines the degree of plant hairiness, and the $T:t$ locus, which determines the presence or absence of red pigment. Haskell (1960) provides information on their segregation in progenies from 25 samples of wild raspberry fruits collected from scattered parts of Britain, and information on the selfed progenies of 23 cultivars is available from the published work of Crane and Lawrence (1931), Grubb (1935), Lewis (1939) and from unpublished work by the writer. . . .

In most populations selection tends to act towards fixation of the most favourable allele, and so the retention of intermediate allelic frequencies at these loci and the consequent occurrence of polymorphism calls for some explanation. Selection would act in favour of the heterozygotes if for example the genes were each associated with a balanced lethal system, or if there were advantages associated with pleiotropic effects of the recessive genes. Alternating directions of selection would also result in both alleles being maintained, and so would exceptionally high mutation rates. An explanation based on possible pleiotropic effects of the recessive genes has been suggested to account for the frequent occurrence of heterozygosity at certain loci in plum cultivars (Williams and Brown, 1956). In the raspberry, however, it has already been postulated that linkage with a semi-lethal gene occurs in the case of both the T and H loci, and accounts for the observed aberrant segregation of these genes (Crane and Lawrence, 1931; Grubb, 1935; Lewis, 1939, 1940). Consequently, if for each of these gene loci a second deleterious gene were found to be linked in repulsion or if the marker genes themselves were found to be linked together in such a way that the postulated lethal genes are in repulsion, then a balanced lethal system or systems would be present, and

Reprinted by permission of the author and publisher from *Heredity* 22: 465–479, 1967.

heterozygosity for the chromosome within which the genes are linked would tend to be maintained. Some evidence for the existence and consequences of this situation is presented here, together with some evidence in the case of the *H* locus that the kind of selection differs in different situations with the result that different genotypes are favoured.

· · ·

Discussion

The data presented provide good evidence for the occurrence and wide distribution of a balanced lethal system in *Rubus idæus*. This could have many of the consequences to the breeding system that are commonly attributed to the presence of chromosome inversions or to heterozygosity for reciprocal chromosome translocations. Heterozygosity, for example, would tend to be maintained, and the necessity for outbreeding reduced if important gene complexes are situated on the chromosome carrying the lethal genes. If this is so, the property of maintaining successful combinations of genes would be particularly advantageous where small but distinct populations of wild raspberries persist in comparative isolation (Jennings, 1964).

The existence of these kinds of breeding mechanism is difficult to detect. In this material, for example, detection of the balanced lethal system depended on the occurrence of marker genes, in *Drosophila* the widespread detection of chromosome inversions was possible only because of the peculiarities of the salivary gland chromosomes, while the frequency of plant populations heterozygous for reciprocal translocations did not become apparent until the advent of cytological surveys (Jones, 1957). In *Vicia faba* only circumstantial evidence indicates that balanced lethal systems might be present; their presence has also been suggested as the means of maintaining tolerance to inbreeding in *Medicago sativa*, *Melilotus officinalis* and *Theobroma cacao* (Rowlands, 1960, 1964).

If a balanced lethal system survives for a long period the survival value of plants homozygous for the chromosome involved will be progressively lowered, because genes which are non-adaptive in the homozygous state will be sheltered from selection and will tend to accumulate. The accumulation of non-adaptive recessive genes in the linkage group studied here is a good indication of this. Consequently, it is possible that the genetic situation may slow the progress of improvement programmes involving inbreeding; alternatively, if the genes which the breeder seeks to make homozygous are not located on the chromosome containing the lethals—possibly genes affecting fruit quality, which are not of adaptive value in nature—the same genetic mechanism may facilitate progress by keeping important adaptive genes heterozygous and thereby avoiding inbreeding depression. It is in fact known that some raspberry varieties—notably Burnetholm Seedling and others believed to be closely related to wild populations—tolerate inbreeding, but it is not clear whether this tolerance has been built up merely by the smallness of the breeding populations from which the varieties were derived, or whether it is mediated by a mechanism such as the one described here in which heterozygosity is maintained.

The families studied showed considerable variation in the survival value of the two forms identified by the marker genes H and h. Two possible explanations for this depend on whether the dominant phenotypes recorded are predominantly heterozygous (Hh) or include an excess of the homozygote (HH) as well. Preponderance of the dominant (H) phenotype could result merely from intensive selection of the heterozygous (Hh) genotype, while an excessive proportion of the recessive (h) form could result simply from a change in selection pressure allowing the homozygous recessive (hh) but not the homozygous dominant (HH) to survive as well. This might occur, for example, if a gene near the H locus were concerned in the production of a substance optimal concentration was optimal where the gene was heterozygous (Hh) but was more favourable in the presence of hh than $HH(sic)$. It is likely that selection pressure would be most intense and hence would discriminate most strongly in favour of the heterozygote where close inbreeding leads to reduction in embryo size. This model therefore suggests a mechanism for regulating the relative frequencies with which heterozygotes survive according to the degree to which the parent is inbred. Such regulation has been described in *Vicia faba* (Drayner, 1959) and in *Medicago cœrulea* (Fyfe, 1957).

Alternatively, the relative survival value of the alleles when homozygous may be affected by environmental conditions and this may explain variations in departure from expected segregation ratios. It is probable that embryos must be balanced in their development with the development of the surrounding seed tissues, and it is conceivable that in different situations different alleles may better achieve this, an idea which has been proposed to explain variations in the survival of alleles at the S locus in blackberries (Jennings, Craig and Topham, 1967).

*   *   *

References

Crane, M. B., and W. J. C. Lawrence. 1931. Inheritance of sex, colour and hairiness in the raspberry, *Rubus idæus* L. *J. Genet.* **24**, 243.

Drayner, J. M. 1959. Self and cross-fertility in field beans (*Vicia faba*). *J. Agric. Sci.* **53**, 387.

Fyfe, J. L. 1957. Relational incompatibility in diploid and tetraploid lucerne. *Nature*, Lond. **179**, 591.

Grubb, N. H. 1922. Commercial raspberries and their classification. *J. Pomol.* **3**, 11–35.

———. 1935. Raspberry breeding at East Malling 1922–34. *J. Pomol.* **13**, 108–134.

Haskell, G. 1960. The raspberry wild in Britain. *Watsonia* **4**, 238.

Jennings, D. L. 1962. Some evidence on the influence of the morphology of raspberry canes upon their liability to be attacked by certain fungi. *Hort. Res.* **1**, 100–111.

———. 1963. Some evidence on the genetic structure of present-day raspberry varieties and some possible implications for further breeding. *Euphytica* **12**, 229–243.

———. 1964. Some evidence of population differentiation in *Rubus idæus* L. *New Phytol.* **63**, 153–157.

———. D. L. Craig, and P. B. Topham, 1967. The role of the male parent in the reproduction of *Rubus. Heredity* **22**, 43–55.

Jones, K. 1957. Some aspects of plant variation—the grasses. In *Progress in the Study of the British Flora*, p. 45. Ed. J. E. Lousely.

Keep, E. 1964. Sepaloidy in the red raspberry, *Rubus idæus* L. *Can. J. Genet. Cytol.* **6**, 52–60.

Lewis, D. 1939. Genetical studies in cultivated raspberries. I. *J. Genet.* **38**, 367–379.

———. 1940. Genetical studies in cultivated raspberries. II. *Genetics* **25**, 278–286.

Mather, K. 1943. *Statistical Analysis in Biology*, p. 186. London: Methuen.

Rowlands, D. G. 1960. Fertility studies in the field bean (*Vicia faba* L.). 1. Cross and self-fertility. *Heredity* **15**, 161–173.

———. 1964. Self incompatibility in sexually propagated cultivated plants. *Euphytica* **13**, 157–162.

Williams, W., and Brown, A. G. 1956. Genetic response to selection in cultivated plants: gene frequencies in *Prunus avium. Heredity* **10**, 237–246.

2 / Natural Selection

Darwin supposed that there had always been an insufficient food supply for all the organisms that could exist, that not all individuals could survive, and that those variants that were best suited to their environment would be the ones in general to succeed and reproduce.

Narise shows that the competitive ability of a species increases with the relative frequency of the parents, which explains how an indigenous species may cope successfully with a few migrant invaders. Pimentel, Feinberg, Wood, and Hayes show that of two species competing in the same ecotype, the dominant is at an evolutionary disadvantage because intraspecific competition becomes the main force acting upon it, whereas the sparse species is under selective pressure from interspecific competition.

Clarke and Sheppard discuss the effect of natural selection on coadapted gene complexes that act on major genes to reduce phenotypic variability; in hybrids the particular combinations of major genes and modifying genes are broken up.

With very small populations, *genetic drift* may result in nonadaptive or neutral gene combinations in spite of selective pressure. A small, isolated population may result from just such a few founders. Simmons describes the effect of this *founders principle* on Drosophila.

The Effect of Relative Frequency of Species in Competition

Takashi Narise

The relation of initial frequency to competition among genes or species is possibly of considerable importance in colonization. It is possible that the strong competitor, when frequencies are equal, may be the weaker competitor if the initial frequency is lower due to the difficulty of finding mates or other frequency dependent factors. This could explain some situations in which a species fails to invade an area occupied by an apparently weaker competitor. In such a situation, the relative frequency of the competitors is the factor that determines the result of competition. Relative frequency dependent selection has been considered theoretically by Haldane (1932), Kimura (1958, 1960), Lewontin (1958), and Wright (1959, 1960), and experimental verification has been given by Levene, Pavlovsky, and Dobzhansky (1954), Lewontin and Matsuo (1963), and Spiess (1961) in *Drosophila*, and by Sokal and Karten (1964) in *Tribolium*. The purpose of this paper is to examine the relative frequency dependent factor in competition *between* two species of *Drosophila*, rather than with species as in the case of these previous authors.

Materials and Methods

Two mutant laboratory strains of *Drosophila melanogaster* and a wild strain of *D. simulans* (Strain No. 3031, 1) collected at Rarotonga, one of the Cook Islands, were used in this experiment. One of the two mutant strains has white eyes from the combined effect of the mutant cinnabar (cn) and brown (bw); the other has white eyes (w) and singed bristles (sn^3). Two-day-old virgin female and male flies of a strain of *D. melanogaster* and of *D. simulans* were mixed together and maintained in half-pint milk bottles for five days; at the end of this time they were discarded. The sex ratio in both species was 1:1 in this experiment. The three levels of population density, 10 pairs, 20 pairs, and 30 pairs, were used in the case of (cn; bw) *D. melanogaster* versus *D. simulans*, but only 10 pairs were used in (w; sn^3) *D. melanogaster*. The relative frequency of *D. simulans* was 0.0, 0.1, 0.2, 0.3, 0.4, 0.5, 0.6, 0.7, 0.8, 0.9, and 1.0 at each level of population density. The number of replications was 30 times for 10 pairs, 40 for 20 pairs, and 40 for 30 pairs, in the cinnabar brown experiment, but only six in the white singed experiment. All flies emerging in the next generation were counted and the competitive ability of *D. simulans* was calculated in the following way.

Let the relative frequency of parents of *D. melanogaster* be p and *D. simulans* be $q = (1 - p)$, and the relative competitive values of *D. melanogaster* to *D. simulans* be $1:k$. The relative frequency of *D. simulans* (r) in

Reprinted by permission of the author and publisher from *Evolution* **19**: 350–354, 1965.

the next generation is $r = (qk)/(p + qk)$ assuming there is no interspecies mating; therefore $k = (rp)/[q(1 - r)]$, where r does not equal one. Since q and r are known, k can be calculated for each replication except for those cultures in which only *D. simulans* emerged. The average number of total emerged flies per bottle in the next generation is shown in Table 1. If the total number of emerged flies in any bottle was less than 300 for 10 pairs, 400 for 20 pairs, and 500 for 30 pairs, the data for this bottle were omitted.

Therefore, the exact number of replications is not the same for each level of parental proportion within like population densities. All experiments were conducted at $25°$ C $\pm$ $1°$.

TABLE 1

Average number of emerged flies per bottle in cn; bw and *D. simulans*

Population density	Species	Relative frequency of *simulans*										
		0.0	0.1	0.2	0.3	0.4	0.5	0.6	0.7	0.8	0.9	1.0
10	cn; bw	571	519	466	418	335	264	240	193	106	37	—
	simulans	—	22	66	102	142	172	271	228	312	350	369
20	cn; bw	801	736	653	600	535	468	388	300	196	115	—
	simulans	—	26	81	127	172	216	291	371	470	571	716
30	cn; bw	846	831	774	664	601	576	450	363	262	162	—
	simulans	—	32	76	129	171	202	248	337	437	521	682

Experimental Results

The average relative frequency of *D. simulans* among the progenies corresponding with each parental relative frequency in the previous generation is shown in Fig. 1. The k values for each relative frequency of *D. simulans* at three levels of population density in competition with (cn; bw) *D. melanogaster* as well as those between (w; sn[3]) *D. melanogaster* versus *D. simulans* are presented in Table 2. In the former, the relative frequency of *D. simulans* increased with an increase of its frequency in the previous generation, although

TABLE 2

Average *k* value of *Drosophila simulans* for each relative frequency in competition between cn; bw and *simulans* and those between w; sn[3] and *simulans*

Species	Population density	Relative frequency of *simulans*								
		0.1	0.2	0.3	0.4	0.5	0.6	0.7	0.8	0.9
cn; bw	10	0.4051	0.5544	0.6303	0.6832	0.7624	0.7210	0.8844	0.8956	1.4627
	20	0.3027	0.4573	0.4947	0.5096	0.4891	0.5504	0.5987	0.6872	0.6521
	30	0.3683	0.4219	0.4711	0.4830	0.4281	0.4853	0.4871	0.5115	0.5474
w; sn[3]	10	0.0154	0.1866	0.1020	0.3024	0.1600	0.1554	0.1431	0.2277	0.1949

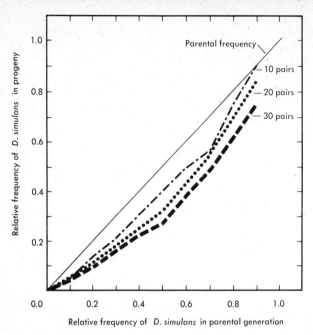

Fig. 1. Relative frequency of *D. simulans* among progenies under competition between (cn; bw) *D. melanogaster* and *D. simulans*.

with the exception of a *D. simulans* of 0.9 using 10 pairs, the increase in relative frequency of progeny was less than the relative frequency of parents as seen in Fig. 1. The *k* values for each frequency in each population density increased with the increase in proportion of *D. simulans* in the previous generation. The parental *D. simulans* of 0.9 with 10 pairs produced a relative frequency of *D. simulans* higher not only than that of (cn; bw) *D. melanogaster* frequency of *D. simulans* higher not only than that of (cn; bw) *D. melano-gaster*, but also higher than parental frequency. Thus, at that frequency the *k* value of *D. simulans* is greater than unity. An analysis of variance on *k* values was made and the result is shown in Table 3. There is a significant deviation between density and between frequency within density. The *k* value

TABLE 3

Analysis of variance on *k* values in competition between cn; bw and *D. simulans*

Source of deviation	D.F.	M.S.
Between densities	2	6.9418*
Between frequencies within densities	24	0.9745*
Between replications within frequencies	891	0.1397

*Significant at 1 per cent level.

is quite different among three densities and among relative frequencies within the same population density.

The relation between k values and the proportion of *D. simulans* in the previous generation was examined for three population densities. The results indicate that the increase of the k value is linearly proportional to the increase in relative frequency of *D. simulans* for 20 pairs and 30 pairs, but not 10 pairs. However, linearity of k values in 10 pairs was established if the value at 0.9 was omitted. The average k value in each frequency and three regression lines fixed for k values in each population density are shown in Fig. 2. The regression line for 10 pairs was calculated for k values with 0.9 value omitted. In competition between (w; sn³) *D. melanogaster* and *D. simulans*, the k values do not differ significantly among relative frequencies (d.f. $= 8, 0.10 > p > 0.05$).

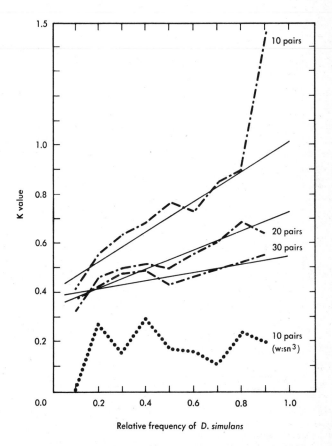

Fig. 2. The k values in different relative frequencies of *D. simulans* and different population densities.

From these experimental results it can be said that for (cn; bw) *D. melanogaster* versus *D. simulans* the competitive ability of *D. simulans* is dependent on the relative frequency in the previous generation. Of special interest in the experiment is that *D. simulans* becomes the strong competitor at 0.9 relative frequency using 10 pairs. In order to find the reason, the number of offspring per pair was examined. Figure 3 shows the average number of offspring per pair at each relative frequency at three population densities. As shown in Fig. 3, the average number of offspring per pair in the (cn; bw) *D. melanogaster* strain increases regularly with a decrease of its parental relative frequency in 20 and 30 pairs. However, for 10 pairs it decreases sharply when there is a very low parental relative frequency. In *D. simulans* the increase of the number of offspring follows the increase of its relative frequency in the three population densities.

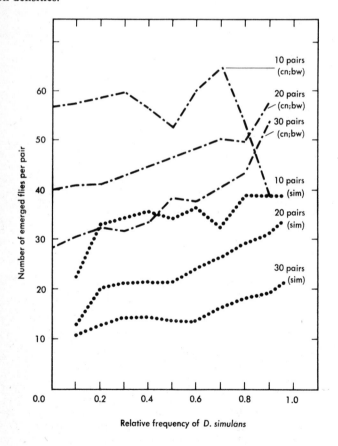

Fig. 3. The number of emerged flies per pair in (cn; bw) *D. melanogaster* and *D. simulans*.

Thus, it is the number of offspring per pair in the (cn; bw) stock that is responsible for the results of the previous section. To discover if mating influenced the competitive ability of the two species, the percentage of females which produce infertile eggs was determined as follows. All female flies kept in half-pint milk bottles during five days were collected and each was maintained another five days in a separate vial. The hatching of eggs was examined in each vial and Table 4 shows the average percentage of females producing infertile eggs. Linear regression coefficients between the percentage of females producing infertile eggs and the relative frequency of parents (Table 5) were all significantly different from zero except in the case of (cn; bw) *D. melanogaster* in a population density of 30 pairs per bottle. It is evident that the percentage of (cn; bw) *D. melanogaster* females which lay infertile eggs increases with increases in the relative frequency of *D. simulans* (except in a population density of 30 pairs), while the percentage of *D. simulans* females laying infertile eggs decreases.

TABLE 4

Average percentage of females which lay infertile eggs

Species	Population density	0.1	0.2	0.3	0.4	0.5	0.6	0.7	0.8	0.9
cn; bw	10	4.4	6.7	7.1	8.2	8.0	10.0	10.0	7.5	20.0
	20	2.8	3.4	4.3	3.7	5.0	6.1	7.5	11.3	10.0
	30	2.4	2.6	3.1	2.8	2.7	2.9	4.4	6.7	8.3
simulans	10	10.0	7.5	8.3	10.0	7.0	7.5	7.1	4.3	4.4
	20	10.0	8.8	6.7	5.6	4.5	4.2	3.9	3.1	2.8
	30	6.7	6.7	3.9	2.9	3.0	2.2	2.4	2.3	2.0

TABLE 5

Linear regression coefficient between the percentage of females which produce infertile eggs and the relative frequency of *D. simulans* in parental generation

Species	*D. simulans*			cn; bw (*D. melanogaster*)		
No. of pairs	10	20	30	10	20	30
Regression Coefficient	−6.15	−8.81	−5.97	12.07	9.62	3.43

The correlation coefficients between the competitive value (k) of *D. simulans* and the percentage of females laying infertile eggs were calculated for the population densities of 10 and 20 pairs per bottle (Table 6). Apparently one of the important frequency dependent factors affecting the competitive ability is the percent of females that successfully mate.

TABLE 6

Correlation coefficient between the competitive value of *D. simulans* and the percentage of females laying infertile eggs in cn; bw and *D. simulans*

Species	cn; bw (D. melanogaster)		D. simulans	
No. of pairs	10	20	10	20
Correlation Coefficient	−0.6527	−0.9191*	0.8484*	0.9910*

*Significant at 1 per cent level.

Discussion

Under laboratory conditions *D. melanogaster* is a considerably stronger competitor than *D. simulans*. Therefore, in order to make the two species more competitive, mutant strains (cn; bw) and (w; sn³) of *D. melanogaster* were used. Even these mutant strains are stronger competitors than *D. simulans* at equal relative frequency; however, at a relative frequency of 0.9, *D. simulans* becomes a stronger competitor than (cn; bw) *D. melanogaster* in experiments using 10 pairs. In the experiment with (cn; bw) *D. melanogaster* and *D. simulans* the competitive ability depends on their relative frequency in the parental generation. However, no relative frequency dependent factor in competition is found between *D. simulans* and (w; sn³) *D. melanogaster*.

The relative frequency of *D. simulans* affects the percentage of females which lay infertile eggs for both *D. simulans* and (cn; bw) *D. melanogaster*, and the correlation between competitive ratio of *D. simulans* and the percentage of infertile females is very high. Therefore, one reason why *D. simulans* becomes competitively stronger at a high relative frequency, in low population density, is the failure of the (cn; bw) *D. melanogaster* females to mate.

From the results of these experiments, it can be seen how a weaker competitor indigenous to an area can prevent a strong competitor from colonizing this area, if migrants are so low in number that the frequency of the indigenous species is always high.

Summary

The effect of relative frequency on competition was studied in two mutant strains of *D. melanogaster* and a strain of *D. simulans*. It was found in a competition experiment between the mutant strain (cn; bw) *D. melanogaster* and *D. simulans* that the competitive ability of a species increased as the relative frequency of its parents increased even to the point of reversing the competitive relationship of the two species when initial proportions are equal. In another competition experiment between (w; sn³) *D. melanogaster* and *D. simulans*, no relative frequency dependent factor on competition was found.

The dependence of competitive ability on relative frequency was explained at least in part by the effect of the relative frequency of parents on mating. The results of these experiments explain how an indigenous species may successfully compete with occasional migrants of a species or strain that under equal relative frequencies would have a competitive advantage.

• • •

Literature Cited

Haldane, J. B. S. 1932. *The Causes of Evolution.* Harper Brothers, New York.

Kimura, M. 1958. On the change of population fitness by natural selection. *Heredity* **12**: 145–167.

———. 1960. *Syudan Idengaku Garion.* Bifukan, Tokyo (Japanese).

Levene, H., O. Pavlovsky, and T. Dobzhansky. 1954. Interaction of the adaptive values in polymorphic experimental populations of *Drosophila pseudoobscura. Evolution* **8**: 335–349.

Lewontin, R. C. 1958. A general method of investigation of equilibrium of gene frequency in populations. *Genetics* **43**: 419–434.

——— and Y. Matsuo. 1963. Interaction of genotypes determining variability in *Drosophila busckii. Proc. Nat Acad. Sci.* **49**: 270–278.

Spiess, E. B. 1961. Chromosome fitness change in experimental populations of *Drosophila persimilis* from timber line in the Sierra Nevada. *Evolution* **15**: 340–351.

Sokal, R. R., and I. Karten. 1964. Competition among genotypes in *Tribolium castaneum* at varying densities and gene frequencies (the black locus). *Genetics* **49**: 195–211.

Wright, S. 1959. Classification of the factor of evolution. Cold Spring Harbor Symp. Quant. Biol. **24**: 16–24.

———. 1960. Genetics, ecology, and selection. In *The Evolution of Life* (S. Tax, ed.). Vol. 1, Univ. Chicago Press.

Selection, Spatial Distribution, and the Coexistence of Competing Fly Species

David Pimentel

Edwin H. Feinberg

Peter W. Wood

John T. Hayes

The competitive exclusion principle states that two species requiring the same resources cannot coexist. This principle is based on the assumption that the competing species themselves and their biotic environment remain genetically constant. From what is known about natural selection and evolution this is a broad assumption. We propose that situations exist in which two species might compete yet still coexist (Pimentel, 1965).

For example, interspecific competitors may change genetically so that both species coexist and utilize the same particular thing in the ecosystem —be it food, space, or other necessary resources. Let us assume that both species are fairly evenly balanced but that species A is slightly superior to species B.

As the numbers of the stronger species are increasing, the numbers of the weaker species are declining and becoming sparse. The abundant individuals of species A at this stage must contend principally with intraspecific competitive selection because there is a greater chance for individuals of this species to interact with their own kind than individuals of the sparse species. Concurrently, species B which is contending primarily with interspecific competitive selective pressure would evolve and improve its ability to compete with its more abundant cohort species A. As species B improves as a competitor its numbers increase and finally B becomes the more abundant species. Thus, the original trend is reversed. After many such oscillations, each change decreasing in intensity, a state of relative stability should result.

Time is essential for such evolution of coexistence to take place between competitors. As mentioned, if two species are fairly similar then fewer changes are necessary to make species B an equal or better competitor than species A. When species A is much stronger than species B, then species B declines rapidly and often does not have sufficient time to evolve.

Although Haldane (1932) did not specifically consider the coexistence of competing species, he pointed out that individuals of a rare species are engaged in competing with other species and struggling against the abiotic environment. Then natural selection is operating effectively, the rare spe-

Reprinted by permission of the authors and The University of Chicago Press from *The American Naturalist* **99**: 97–109, 1965. © 1965 by the University of Chicago. All rights reserved. Published 1965.

cies evolves and becomes better able to contend with its competitors and other environmental factors. This is not usually so with a dominant species, reported Haldane, because these individuals are found in dense associations in which intraspecific selection may be biologically advantageous for the individual but ultimately disastrous for the species (see also Huxley, 1948). Certainly such intraspecific competition would seldom be favorable for a species especially relative to its ability to compete against the sparse species.

The chances of the sparse species persisting and not dwindling to extinction because of competitive pressure depends upon the variability in the sparse species population, and how much time is available for evolution and subsequent improvement. With suitable variability and sufficient time the sparse species under interspecific selective pressure should be able to make the necessary changes so that it can meet the pressures of its competitor.

The evolutionary adjustment between the competing species would function in either a non-random or random distribution. The sparse species, non-randomly distributed in scattered small colonies, would have an advantage because this distribution provides the most favorable opportunity for evolutionary advance (Wright, 1937).

Further evidence in support of this idea comes from the existence of genotypic strains of *Tribolium confusum* and *Tribolium castaneum*, which have different competitive abilities. Lerner and Ho (1961) report that either *T. confusum* or *T. castaneum* will win in competition depending on which genotypic strains are competed against one another. To keep these two competing species co-existing in a laboratory situation would require only the manipulation of a proportion of the genotypes making up each species population; competitive ability can be selected for (Moore, 1952).

Our aim in this study was to experimentally investigate the idea that the dominant species in competition remains relatively static in its interspecific competitive ability and that the sparse species evolves to become the better competitor and eventually the dominant species.

•   •   •

Discussion

The coexistence of the housefly and blowfly populations in the 16-cell system did not occur. A 30-cell system is now under study. More space and larger populations should provide the necessary time for evolution and coexistence of these species in the same ecological niche. The preliminary trends in the 16-cell system, however, were most encouraging. We had predicted that the sparse species would evolve and become a better competitor and that the dominant species would remain relatively the same in its interspecific competitive ability. This happened. The sparse blowfly population evolved and became a significantly better competitor; the dominant housefly population remained static in its competitive ability.

Although the results were most encouraging we regret that more than one 16-cell population system was not used. Our procedure was dictated by the time required for maintenance and study of such systems.

A question which we raised was that of adding wild genes to the population to prevent inbreeding and deterioration. This procedure may have added a favorable set of genes. To avoid this possibility in the two single-cell population systems which persisted for more than 70 weeks, no outside genes were added. Both still evolved in a manner similar to the multi-cell system. For this reason, we feel confident that selection and evolution were responsible for the change in dominance in the multi-cell system and not the introduced genes.

The persistent alternation of dominance in the two single-cell population systems which existed for more than 70 weeks or more than 35 fly generations suggested that the feed-back mechanism was operating here. The experimental populations set up from stocks removed from these two parent populations also substantiated this. The results from all the tests reported here tend to support the idea proposed that two competing species can occupy the same niche, but more research is needed to understand the mechanism.

Summary

Interspecific competitors may change genetically with the result that competing species can coexist in the same ecosystem. As a competing species becomes the dominant species, it is at an evolutionary disadvantage because intraspecific competition is the main selective force acting on it. The sparse species, however, because it is under selective pressure from interspecific competition has an evolutionary advantage. Given sufficient time a genetic adjustment between the competing species should result.

To test this theory two competitors, the housefly and blowfly, were released in opposite corners of a multi-celled cage. At first the housefly population suppressed the blowfly population, but in time the blowfly increased, became the dominant species and eventually caused the extinction of the housefly. A genetic check on the blowfly population when it started its comeback showed that it had evolved into a more effective competitor than the housefly. To see if these two species can evolve, coexist and occupy the same niche, a multi-cell cage with increased space-time structure is now under investigation.

Literature Cited

Haldane, J. B. S., 1932, *The Causes of Evolution.* Longmans, Green and Co., New York, London, and Toronto. 235 p.

Huxley, J., 1943, *Evolution and Modern Synthesis.* Harper & Bros., New York and London. 645 p.

Kilpatrick, J. W., and H. F. Schoof, 1956, Fly production in treated and untreated privies. *Publ. Health Rep. (U.S.)* **71**: 787–796.

Lerner, J. M., and F. K. Ho, 1961, Genotype and competitive ability of *Tribolium* species. *Am. Naturalist* **45**: 329–343.

Moore, J. A., 1952, Competition between *Drosophila melanogaster* and *Drosophila simulans*. II. The improvement of competitive ability through selection. *Proc. Natl. Acad. Sci. U.S.* **38**: 813–817.

Pimentel, D., 1965, Population ecology and the genetic feed-back mechanism. *Genetics Today* **2**: 483–488.

———, W. P. Nagel, and J. L. Madden, 1963. Space-time structure of the environment and the survival of parasite-host systems. *Am. Naturalist* **97**: 141–167.

Quarterman, K. D., W. C. Baker, and J. A. Jensen, 1949, The importance of sanitation in municipal fly control. *Am. J. Trop. Med.* **29**: 973–982.

Wright, S., 1937. The distribution of gene frequencies in populations. *Proc. Natl. Acad. Sci. U.S.* **23**: 307–32.

Interactions between Major Genes and Polygenes in the Determination of the Mimetic Patterns of *Papilio dardanus*

C. A. Clarke

P. M. Sheppard

Recent genetic work on *Papilio dardanus* (Clarke and Sheppard, 1960a, b) has shown that the major allelomorphs controlling the mimetic patterns produce a good likeness to the model only in the gene complex of races that possess the mimic. In hybrids between races possessing a particular mimetic pattern and those not possessing it, the mimetic pattern controlled by the gene is less perfect, indicating that within any one race the gene complex is adjusted by natural selection in such a way that a good mimetic pattern is produced.

The Madagascan race of *Papilio dardanus* is particularly useful for such studies since it is monomorphic, the female being like the males in general appearance and non-mimetic (Clarke and Sheppard, 1960c). In our previous communication some data on hybrids involving the Madagascan race were reported. We have recently been able to obtain more information about this race (*meriones*) with the help of Mr. Michael Wells, who in 1959 undertook an expedition from South Africa to Madagascar on our behalf. He sent us both larvae and adult insects, and from this material we were able to breed a few subsequent generations. We found, however, that *meriones* was much more difficult to rear than the other races; females did not lay so readily, and many larvae never started to feed and died soon after hatching. *Choisya* was preferred to *Citrus*, though the latter is one of the food plants in the wild. The present paper reports some of the results obtained by hybridizing this stock with others from South Africa (race *cenea*) and from Kenya (race *polytrophus*).

• • •

Discussion

The extreme variability in the F_1 hybrids compared with the main African and Madagascan stocks and the even greater variability in the F_2 (including the difference between the presumed homozygous yellow insects and the pure Madagascan stock) indicate that both races have coadapted gene complexes which insures a low degree of variability in the phenotypic expressions of the major genes. In the F_1 and F_2 generations genes have been introduced by hybridization so that the gene complex is no longer coadapted and con-

Reprinted by permission of the authors and publisher from *Evolution* 17: 404–413, 1963.

siderable variability results. Of even more interest is the variability in the homozygous mimetic forms resulting from backcrossing the F_1 hybrids to the South African stock. In these the mimetic resemblance to South African models is in some instances remarkably poor, the appearance of insects of the same genotype as far as the major genes are concerned differing markedly between broods (and even between individuals within one brood). There can be no doubt that the high degree of variability and the poor mimicry result from introducing part of the gene complex of the Madagascan stock. Since this stock is monomorphic, it cannot have been adjusted by natural selection to produce good mimicry in the presence of the appropriate major genes for the mimetic patterns. The crosses reported in this paper therefore supply yet more evidence that the pattern in *Papilio dardanus*, whether one considers the mimetic or non-mimetic patterns, is stabilized by natural selection which results in a highly coadapted gene complex, so that the major genes produce the most advantageous effects.

Summary

1. In the butterfly *Papilio dardanus* racial crosses have been carried out between some of the mimetic forms found on the African mainland and the malelike non-mimetic race *meriones* from Madagascar. F_1, F_2, and backcross hybrids were obtained.

2. Great variability was found in the F_1 and greater still in the F_2 hybrids compared with that in the parent races. This indicates that each race has a coadapted gene complex which insures a low degree of variability in the phenotypic expression of the major genes, and that this is markedly disturbed in these race crosses.

3. There was marked infertility of the F_2 parents, and the data suggest that *meriones* merits designation as a subspecies.

4. In the backcrosses to the main African stock there was great variability in the homozygous mimetic forms, the mimicry often being very poor. This is attributed to the introduction of the Madagascar stock which, as it is non-mimetic, cannot have been adjusted to produce good mimicry in the presence of the appropriate major genes for the mimetic pattern.

5. These crosses supply more evidence that both the mimetic and non-mimetic patterns in *Papilio dardanus* are stabilized by natural selection, which results in highly coadapted gene complexes whereby the major genes produce the most advantageous effects.

• • •

Literature Cited

Clarke, C. A., and P. M. Sheppard. 1960a. The evolution of mimicry in the butterfly *Papilio dardanus*, Brown. *Heredity* **14**: 163–173.

—— 1960b. Supergenes and mimicry. *Heredity* **14**: 175–185.

—— 1960c. The genetics of *Papilio dardanus*, Brown. 111. Race *antinorii* from Abyssinia and Race *meriones* from Madagascar. *Genetics* **45**: 683–698.

——. 1962. Disruptive selection and its effect on a metrical character in the butterfly *Papilio dardanus*. *Evolution* **16**: 214–226.

Experiments on Random Genetic Drift and Natural Selection in *Drosophila pseudoobscura*

A. Solima Simmons

Dobzhansky and Levene (1951) and Dobzhansky and Pavlovsky (1953, 1957) observed a remarkable variability in the action of natural selection in replicate experimental populations of *Drosophila pseudoobscura*. These experimental populations were polymorphic for gene arrangements (inversions) in the third chromosomes. Such polymorphic populations can be made in two ways—all the chromosomes may be derived from wild ancestors collected in a single geographic locality, or they may come from geographically remote populations. Experimental populations of uniform geographic origin behave uniformly and predictably. The changes in the chromosome frequencies that occur in such populations are, within the limits of sampling errors, the same in replicate populations, provided, of course, that the environmental conditions are properly controlled. It is otherwise in populations of mixed geographic origin. With environments just as carefully controlled, the effects of natural selection may be divergent in replicate experimental populations.

The authors referred to above have interpreted these results as follows. The gene pool, the genetic background, is relatively less variable in populations of uniform origin than it is in populations of mixed origin. In nature, the chromosomal polymorphism is balanced, owing to heterosis in the heterokaryotypes. The action of natural selection in populations of geographically uniform origin causes the same genetic equilibrium to be reached. In populations of mixed origin the relative fitness of the karyotypes varies on different genetic backgrounds. Natural selection acts differently in different populations, and in different generations in the same population. This hypothetical interpretation has been tested in two ways. First, Dobzhansky and Pavlovsky (1957) reasoned that the genetic backgrounds in replicate populations are likely to be more variable, other things being equal, if the populations are derived from small numbers of founders than if they are derived from numerous founders. Therefore, the variability may be expected to be, and was actually found to be, greater in the populations descended from fewer founders. Secondly, if the numbers of the founders are the same, the variability in replicate populations should be greater if the founders come from a genetically more variable source than if they come from a less variable source. Dobzhansky and Spassky (1962) showed that the results of natural selections are more divergent in "multichromosomal" than in "bichromosomal" populations.

Reprinted by permission of the author and publisher from *Evolution* 20: 100–103, 1966.

The present article describes the results of a third, still different, test imposed on the hypothesis. Suppose that we have several replicate experimental populations of mixed genetic origin which have diverged genetically. One of these populations may be subdivided into several new replicates of common, non-hybrid, origin. Two populations can be hybridized, and another series of replicates is then arranged using founders of hybrid origin. One may expect that the replicates of non-hybrid origin will produce less variable results than those of hybrid origin. As shown below, this is what, in fact, is observed.

The Experiments

Dobzhansky and Spassky (1962) made, in March of 1957, five experimental populations of *Drosophila pseudoobscura*, taking as founders flies from the F_2 generation of hybrids between 10 strains with the AR gene arrangement in the third chromosomes derived from the population of Mather, California, and 10 strains with the PP gene arrangement from the population of Austin, Texas. Each experimental population was started with 20 founders, 10 virgin females and 10 males. The experimental populations were kept in wooden population cages of the usual design. All the populations were allowed to

TABLE 1

Frequencies, in per cent, of AR chromosomes in the populations

Cycles	Hybrid populations					Mean
	1	2	3	4	5	
I	72.7	72.7	81.0	81.7	80.0	77.60
II	86.7	69.7	80.0	82.0	81.3	79.93
III	87.7	88.7	79.0	88.0	74.0	83.46
IV	80.0	69.3	65.3	81.0	68.0	72.73
V	69.0	79.0	80.0	77.7	73.0	75.73
VI	79.0	74.0	69.3	89.3	79.0	78.13
VII	67.0	78.7	87.7	88.0	81.0	80.46
VIII	80.0	78.0	68.0	86.3	82.0	78.87
IX	69.7	73.0	77.3	84.0	79.0	76.60
Mean	76.85	75.89	76.40	84.22	77.48	78.17
	Non-hybrid populations					
I	78.7	72.3	68.0	74.0	70.7	72.73
II	68.3	67.3	69.3	67.0	67.3	67.86
III	71.3	76.0	69.0	72.7	71.3	72.06
IV	72.7	70.0	71.0	73.0	72.7	71.86
V	71.3	72.7	69.0	70.7	68.0	70.33
VI	69.3	71.7	69.3	70.0	72.0	70.46
VII	73.7	68.7	72.0	70.0	71.0	71.06
VIII	70.0	69.3	71.0	69.0	72.7	70.40
IX	72.0	69.3	72.7	70.0	71.3	71.06
Mean	71.92	70.81	70.15	70.70	70.77	70.87

breed for about four months. At the end of this first "cycle," a sample of 20 flies, 10 virgin females and 10 males, was taken from each population. These flies served as founders of the second cycle, of about the same duration. After nine cycles, the five originally replicate populations were found to have diverged considerably. One of the populations, no. 3, had 63 per cent of AR and 37 per cent of PP chromosomes. Population no. 4 had 94 per cent AR and six per cent PP chromosomes. These populations were the source of the material for the experiments reported below.

Ten virgin females from population no. 3 of Dobzhansky and Spasṣky were crossed to 10 males from their population no. 4, and males from no. 3 to females from no. 4. The F_1 generations were pooled, and an F_2 generation raised. In the F_2, five groups of 10 pairs were taken at random, allowed to reproduce in culture bottles, with transfers every second day to fresh cultures, and then roughly 1000 flies of both sexes were taken to serve as parents of each of the five replicate "hybrid populations," designated by numbers 1 to 5 in Tables 1 and 2. Five groups of 10 pairs were taken from population no. 3 of Dobzhansky and Spassky, treated similarly to the above except that they were not outcrossed, and served as parents of the "non-hybrid populations" nos. 1 to 5, in Tables 1 and 2. All experimental populations were kept at 25°C. The operation of sampling 10 pairs of flies from each of my 10 experimental populations was repeated in each of nine cycles begun at the following times:

Cycle I —January 1961
Cycle II —May 1961
Cycle III —October 1961
Cycle IV —March 1962
Cycle V —November 1962
Cycle VI —April 1963
Cycle VII —September 1963
Cycle VIII—February 1964
Cycle IX —August 1964

TABLE 2

Variances of the frequencies of the chromosomes

Cycles	Hybrid	Non-hybrid	Populations	Hybrid	Non-hybrid
I	20.65	15.91	1	58.18	9.12
II	39.25	0.92	2	36.29	6.89
III	43.67	6.76	3	53.07	2.47
IV	52.49	1.74	4	15.51	4.76
V	21.35	3.43	5	22.58	3.61
VI	55.36	1.64			
VII	73.35	3.63			
VIII	46.41	2.18			
IX	30.54	1.91			

At the end of each cycle, samples of eggs deposited in each population were taken, and allowed to develop in regular culture bottles with ample food. The chromosomes in the salivary glands of 150 larvae from each sample (i.e., 300 third chromosomes) were examined in preparations stained with aceto-orcein. The percentages of the chromosomes with the AR gene arrangement found in the samples are reported in Table 1. The frequencies of PP chromosomes are, evidently, the remainder to 100 per cent.

Inspection of Table 1 shows very clearly that among the hybrid populations the frequencies of AR chromosomes have varied greatly in different populations of the same cycle, and in different cycles in the same population. The frequencies in non-hybrid populations were more uniform. The maximum and minimum percentages in the hybrid populations were about 89 and 65 per cent respectively, while in the non-hybrid ones they were 79 and 67 per cent. The mean percentages in different populations and different cycles varied from 72.7 to 84.2 in the hybrids, and only from 67.9 to 72.7 in the non-hybrid populations. The smallest chi-square for heterogeneity among the five hybrid populations is found in the first cycle, namely 14.27. For four degrees of freedom, this has less than one per cent probability of being due to chance. Contrasting with this, the largest chi-square among the non-hybrid populations, found also in the first cycle, is 9.66. The probability of this being due to chance is almost five per cent. Among the hybrid populations, no. 4 gave least variable results in different cycles; the chi-square for eight degrees of freedom, 28.02, has a probability much less than one per cent of being due to chance. Among the non-hybrid populations, apparently the most variable in different cycles is no. 1. The chi-square value is 10.88, which is, for eight degrees of freedom, not significant.

The same relationships can be seen even more clearly in Table 2. Without a single exception, the variances for different populations within a cycle are greater in the hybrid than in the non-hybrid populations. The same is true of the variances for the different cycles within a population.

Discussion

The frequencies of the AR and PP chromosomes in populations, whether natural or experimental, are influenced by natural selection. The difference in fitness between the heterokaryotype and the homokaryotypes is, at 25°C., quite large (Dobzhansky and Pavlovsky, 1957). The sampling errors introduced by taking 20 flies (40 chromosomes) at the beginning of each cycle in our experiments should be evened up, owing to the action of natural selection, by the end of the cycle. This is equally true for the hybrid and the non-hybrid populations. What, then, is the origin of the differences between the replicate populations, and why are these differences observed among the hybrid but not among non-hybrid populations? The hypothesis first suggested by Dobzhansky and Pavlovsky (1953) makes the situation understandable. The divergence of the replicates arises not from the third chromosomes with the AR and PP gene arrangements, but from the genetic background, the remainder of the genetic system. The differences stem from the founders of of the populations which, being few in numbers, bring different collections "modifier" genes. The "founder principle" is a special case of Wright's random genetic drift, operating, in my experiments, at the beginning of each cycle.

My experimental populations were derived originally from hybrids between California and Texas populations of Dobzhansky and Spassky (1962). These authors have observed a genetic divergence between replicate populations of this hybrid origin, and the divergence, in their experiments, increased with time. The variability of the genetic background, introduced by the hybridization, will, however, decrease with time, especially because at the beginning of each cycle each population passes through the "funnel" of a limited number of founders. Progressive depletion of the genetic variability will eventually make the populations of geographically mixed origins about equivalent to non-hybrid populations. It is really this inference that is tested in my experiments. Replicate populations derived from a single stabilized population failed to diverge. Those derived from hybridization of two such populations did diverge. The hybrid populations of Dobzhansky and Spassky were evidently about as different from each other in their genetic backgrounds as were the geographic populations, the hybrids of which served as the source material for the experimental populations. The random genetic drift has operated, via the limited numbers of the founders of the experimental populations, in the experiment of Dobzhansky and Spassky. It has been induced to operate again in my experiments.

Summary

Ten experimental populations, polymorphic for AR and PP gene arrangements in the third chromosomes were made, starting each with 20 "founders," 10 females and 10 males. Five of these populations were derived from hybrids between two experimental populations described by Dobzhansky and Spassky (1962), which were themselves derived from hybridization of flies from California with those from Texas. The other five populations were made from one of the experimental populations. The five populations of hybrid origin showed a significant genetic divergence, while the five non-hybrid populations showed no divergence. These results are understandable, and were in fact predicted, on the basis of the hypothesis of Dobzhansky and Pavlovsky (1953) involving interaction of natural selection with the random genetic drift (founders principle).

Literature Cited

Dobzhansky, T. and H. Levene. 1951. Development of heterosis through natural selection in experimental populations of *Drosophila pseudoobscura*. *Amer. Nat.* **85**: 247–264.

———— and O. Pavlovsky. 1953. Indeterminate outcome of certain experiments on Drosophila populations. *Evolution* **7**: 198–210.

———— 1957. An experimental study of interactions between genetic drift and natural selection. *Evolution* **11**: 311–319.

———— and N. Spassky. 1962. Genetic drift and natural selection in experimental populations of *Drosophila pseudoobscura*. *Proc. Nat. Acad. Sci.* **48**: 148–156.

3 / Ecological Adaptation

Various environmental factors may act as agents in natural selection. Some, like temperature, moisture, light, and chemical compounds in the air, soil, and water, are features of the physical environment; others, like predation, crowding, and the symbiotic effects of one organism on another, are features of the biotic environment. If, as the result of selection, a trait or characteristic benefits a particular organism, it is regarded as an adaptation.

Maclean shows how the double-banded courser is adapted to life under such extremes of heat and dessication as are found in the Kalahari Desert. Gerson points out that two closely related diaspidid scale insects have adapted differently to dryness and that climatic conditions modify what appears to be a common habitat.

Poulson describes steps in the reduction of the eye in a series of related genera of cave fish and emphasizes mutation with relaxed selection. Discussing soil conditions, Jowett shows that grass populations can become adapted to life on land with a high lead content and a low concentration of calcium and phosphorus.

The biotic environment must not be neglected. Color differences and the ability to change color are adaptations to predators, as Lee shows, and Faegri points out that flower structure in the Proteaceae has evolved together with pollinating systems.

The Breeding Biology and Behaviour of the Double-Banded Courser *Rhinoptilus africanus* (Temminck)

G. L.Maclean

Introduction

Apart from that described in a short communication by Moreau & Moreau (1937), very little biological work has been done on the Double-banded Courser *Rhinoptilus africanus* and indeed on the subfamily Cursoriinae as a whole. The present study, which was made from October 1964 to April 1966 in the Kalahari Gemsbok National Park, South Africa, formed part of a programme on the biology of desert animals supported by a grant to Dr. T. J. Cade of Cornell University, New York, from the United States Public Health Service, ES 00008 (Environmental Health).

The Gemsbok Park lies at 3,200 ft. a.s.l. in the southwestern corner of the Kalahari region in the extreme north of Cape Province, sandwiched between South West Africa and Bechuanaland. The area, which has been described by Leistner (1959), consists of red sand dunes covered with grass and shrubs or fair sized trees. The dunes, which are dissected by two large dry rivers, the Auob in the west and the Nossob in the east, are lined for most of their length by large trees. On the eastern banks of both rivers, mainly in their southern reaches, is a discontinuous strip of exposed stony calcrete varying in width from a few yards to half a mile. The calcrete is covered with small woody shrublets between six inches and a foot high, consisting largely of *Salsola tuberculata*, *Aizoon fruticosum*, *Monechma australe*, *Eriocephalus pubescens* and *Pteronia mucronata*.

The mean annual in rainfall in the study area from 1959–64 was 226.0 mm.; the highest summer temperature measured was 43.4°C.; the lowest winter temperature was −9.7°C. . . .

Habitat, Status, and Movements

The Double-banded Courser is almost confined to the calcrete, which is usually bare between the shrublets, except after good rains, when a cover of grass and herbs fills the spaces. The barest areas, which occur near the wind-mills where drinking antelopes have trampled the vegetation, are usually avoided by the coursers, except after rain, when the cover is too dense on the rest of the calcrete. The bare areas are then favoured for nesting, indicating that good visibility is an essential feature of the nest-site.

Reprinted by permission of the author and the British Ornithologists' Union from *The Ibis* **109**: 556–569, 1967.

Coursers may occasionally be found in the dune country and may even nest there, but only in the barest areas, because the vegetation is usually much taller and denser than that of the calcrete. The red sand of the dunes, furthermore, is a relatively unsuitable background for the otherwise cryptic buff and black of the coursers' plumage and for the grey egg. The Double-banded Courser is definitely a bird of stony terrain, both in the Kalahari and elsewhere over its range in South and East Africa (Mackworth-Praed & Grant 1952).

Because of its restricted habitat, *Rhinoptilus africanus* is not common in the Kalahari sandveld. Its numbers fluctuate considerably suggesting that the birds are at least partly migratory. The nature of their movements is not clear, but numbers are lowest after good rains when the vegetation on the calcrete is densest, and also when conditions are very dry, as in January 1966. Twenty-one birds were ringed, but none was recovered.

. . .

Discussion

The coursers (Glareolidae, Cursoriinae) are largely confined to desert or semi-desert regions (Moreau 1964). The Double-banded Courser *Rhinoptilus africanus* ranges from the drier Karroo in the southeastern part of South Africa to the fringe of the Namib Desert in the west. Like most other coursers, its movements are dependent on environmental changes, but it is more static than the other common courser of the Kalahari, namely Burchell's Courser *Cursorius rufus*. Its ability to remain and to breed throughout the year indicates the existence of an adequate insect supply at all times in the Kalahari. The other small insectivorous bird species of the Kalahari do not, however, breed all year round, but only after rain; *Rhinoptilus africanus* lays but a single egg per clutch, possibly so that it can rear the single chick even when the season is very dry. The partly nocturnal feeding habits of *R. africanus* must also enable it to utilize a food supply which is not available to the strictly diurnal insectivorous birds.

In an extreme climate like that of the Kalahari, food is less of a problem than overheating and desiccation in summer. Adult coursers must have remarkable heat-tolerance to be able to withstand the effects of direct sunlight for two hours or more without visible signs of distress. This heat-tolerance is less well developed in the young, whose heat-stress behaviour is paralleled by that of small arboreal passerines. I have seen adult *Parisoma subcaeruleum* (Muscicapidae) and *Eremomela icteropygialis* (Sylviidae) suffer collapse from heat prostration when exposed to the sun in the same way as courser chicks. These two passerine species nest in shaded sites and, like the courser chicks, keep to the shade as far as possible throughout the daylight hours.

Behavioural heat-loss mechanisms in *Rhinoptilus africanus* are similar to those of most birds. Heat tolerance must therefore be partly physiological. Whether this includes a method of reducing evaporation is not known, but evaporation is essential for cooling during panting. Water loss is greatly increased in hot weather. Since coursers do not drink, their food must be the sole source of water. This undoubtedly imposes a salt load on the birds. Since the kidneys of birds excrete only 0.3% salt, their function must be augmented by salt glands which, in some birds, can secrete up to 5% salt (Schmidt-Nielsen 1959). The evidence for the presence of functional salt glands in coursers is the white crystalline deposit around their nostrils. This is an important field for further study.

The degree of parental care is also admirably adapted to the harsh environment, especially in summer. The adults provide the greatest coverage of the egg or chick during the day to protect them from direct sunlight. More accurate data on radiation temperatures in the Kalahari and the effects of radiation on the egg are needed to elucidate some of the observed behaviour in coursers further.

Except during distraction and threat displays, the behaviour of *R. africanus* is cryptic. The birds are difficult to see and their movements unobtrusive. Their reluctance to fly has been remarked on (McLachlan & Liversidge 1957) and reflects the birds' tendency towards inconspicuous behaviour; in contrast to this, *Cursorius rufus* flies readily. The two species are further compared in Table 1.

TABLE 1

Ecological and biological differences between *R. africanus* and *C. rufus,* the two common courser species of the Kalahari

Rhinoptilus africanus	*Cursorius rufus*
Habitat stony with low shrubs	Habitat bare and open, even to flat salt pans
Bill short, not used for digging	Bill long, used for digging
Probably exclusively insectivorous	Largely insectivorous, but may eat seeds at times
Plumage mottled; adapted to disruptive background	Plumage plain; adapted to uniform background
Solitary and largely resident	Gregarious and migratory
Seldom calls in flight	Commonly calls in flight
One egg per clutch	Two eggs per clutch

The ability of *Rhinoptilus africanus* to orientate to the nest and to find displaced eggs compares with that of other Charadrii (cf. Walters 1956). The ability to find displaced eggs is probably due in part to the total absence of a nest scrape. At one nest, for instance, the egg was moved by the birds a distance of 25 cm. in a 24-hour period in the process of egg-turning; the egg was laid on hard smooth ground without stones, on which it would have been difficult to make a scrape. I have noted similar natural egg-displacement in *Cursorius rufus*, which also makes no nest scrape.

Table 1 shows that *R. africanus* and *C. rufus* are separated ecologically in the Kalahari. Neither occurs in the dunes (except rarely), so that neither is truly a bird of the Kalahari sandveld. It is only along the river beds and in the areas of exposed calcrete the these birds tend to spread into the sandveld. *C. rufus* occurs only in the barest areas of the river beds and calcrete, where it seldom encroaches on the more shrubby habitat favoured by *R. africanus*. The larger clutch size of *C. rufus* may be associated with more seasonal breeding, but we know too little at present about the biology of this species in South Africa to do more than make a tentative suggestion to this effect.

The behaviour of *R. africanus* has much in common with that of the Burhinidae (cf. Maclean, 1966). In both families that accent is on concealment. Most of the comfort movements and ritualized intention movements are similar. It is probably incidental, however, that both families tend to be nocturnal.

The tossing of small objects around the egg (or eggs) by the departing bird at nest relief is a typically charadriiform behaviour pattern to which little attention has been drawn. I have also found it to be extremely well developed in the Pteroclidae, which show so many other charadriiform characteristics (Maclean, in prep.) that it may be regarded as an ordinal character. Hall (1959) mentions this behaviour, which he calls "side-throwing," in *Vanellus* (*Hoplopterus*) *armatus* and I have also seen it in *Vanellus coronatus* and a number of Charadriinae. Skead (1955) also noted that the nest of *V. coronatus* becomes filled with small objects during the course of incubation, but failed to observe how this was done. In most Charadrii, it occurs at nest relief only, but it may be performed as a displacement activity before an incubating bird is disturbed from the nest. The adaptive value of side-throwing is not immediately clear, but it may indicate how nest-building originated (cf. Hall 1959).

* * *

Summary

In the southwestern part of the Kalahari region, the Double-banded Courser *Rhinoptilus africanus* is restricted to stony terrain with low vegetation and good visibility. Nests are always exposed, usually on flat ground, less often in hollows or slopes, and seldom on rises. Sixty per cent of nests were among mammal droppings.

Nest relief is rapid and occurs every two hours or so; side-throwing of small objects around the nest by the relieved bird is part of the ceremony. Incubation of the single egg takes about 26 days. The newly hatched chick is weak and is fed exclusively by the parents for the first few days. It can fly at about six weeks of age. Breeding seems to be continuous, regardless of weather and season.

The calls, displays, comfort movements and ritualized intention movements are described and analysed as far as possible. Adult coursers are subjected to an intense heat load in summer, and have a number of behavioural heat-loss mechanisms which are described and discussed.

   R. africanus and *Cursorius rufus* (both common coursers of the Kalahari) are briefly compared.

• • •

References

Brown, R. G. B. 1962. The aggressive and distraction behaviour of the Western Sandpiper *Ereunetes mauri*. *Ibis* **104**: 1–12.

Daanje, A. 1950. On locomotory movements in birds and the intention movements derived from them. *Behaviour* **3**: 48–98.

Hall, K. R. L. 1959. A study of the Blacksmith Plover *Hoplopterus armatus* in the Cape Town area: I. Distribution and breeding data. *Ostrich* **30**: 117–126.

Leistner, O. A. 1959. Preliminary list of plants found in the Kalahari Gemsbok National Park. *Koedoe* **2**: 152–172.

McKinney, F. 1965. The comfort movements of the Anatidae. *Behaviour* **25**: 120–220.

Mackworth-Praed, C. W. and C. H. B. Grant. 1952. *Birds of Eastern and North Eastern Africa*. African Handbook of Birds, Series I, Vol. I. London: Longmans, Green & Co.

McLachlan, G. R. and R. Liversidge. 1957. *Roberts' Birds of South Africa*. South Africa: Central News Agency.

Maclean, G. L. 1966. Studies on the behaviour of a young Cape Dikkop *Burhinus capensis* (Lichtenstein) reared in captivity. *Proc. II pan-Afr. Orn. Congr. Ostrich Suppl.* **6**.

——— and V. C. Moran. 1965. The choice of nest site in the White-fronted Sandplover *Charadrius marginatus* Vieillot. Ostrich **36**: 63–72.

Moreau, R. E. 1964. Courser, in *A New Dictionary of Birds* (Ed. A. L. Thomson): 158–159. London & New York: Nelson.

——— and W. M. Moreau. 1937. Biological and other notes on some East African birds. *Ibis* **(14) 1**: 152–174.

Schmidt-Nielsen, K. 1959. Salt glands. *Sci. Amer.* **200**: 109–116.

Skead, C. J. 1955. A study of the Crowned Plover *Stephanibyx coronatus coronatus* (Boddaert). *Ostrich* **25**: 88–98.

Walters, J. 1956. Eirückgewinnung und Nistplatzorientierung bei See- und Flussregenpfeifer (*Charadrius alexandrinus* und *dubius*). *Limosa* **29**: 103–129.

Interrelationships of Two Scale Insects on Citrus

Uri Gerson

Abstract

The interrelationships of 2 diaspidid scale insects of the genus *Parlatoria*, infesting citrus, were investigated during several years in the field. It was found that *P. pergandii* Comstock was more numerous in the summer, *P. cinerea* Hadden in the winter. With reference to the respective geographical distribution of these species, it is postulated that climatic conditions annually modify the common habitat and thus determine the outcome.

Introduction

Competitive displacement and coexistence among insects were recently reviewed and discussed by DeBach (1966). Quite a few cases of competitive displacement or of actual or apparent coexistence between two or more species of insects or of other organisms have been recorded (DeBach 1966), but the scale insects (Homoptera, Coccoidea), and particularly the Diaspididae, have been very little studied in this context. The few known cases are reviewed briefly below.

Schweig and Gruenberg (1936) discussed competition between the Florida red scale, *Chrysomphalus ficus* Ashm. [= *C. aonidum* (L.)] and the California red scale [*Aonidiella aurantii* (Mask.)] on citrus in Palestine. The former was usually dominant, a fact attributed to the higher fecundity of Florida red scale females and to the greater resistance of its crawlers to adverse climatic conditions.

Flanders (1956) noted that the California red scale and the yellow scale [*Aonidiella citrina* (Coq.)] coexist on citrus in Southeast Asia, but "struggled for existence" in California. He postulated that "key to the harmony existing in Southeast Asia between yellow and red scale and between them and the citrus tree appears to be the regulating (police) action of the natural enemies." In California, however, yellow scale is attacked by more efficient parasites than the red scale, hence the latter scale insect is slowly replacing the former. DeBach (DeBach and Sundby 1963) also discussed this displacement, but suggested that competition must have been limited to a completely nonaggressive search for settling, feeding and growing sites of the crawlers of the two diaspidids, which become sessile within 24 hours after hatching.

Reprinted by permission of the author and publisher from *Ecology* **48**: 872–873, 1967.

It has recently become known that populations of the chaff scale, *Parlatoria pergandii* Comst. are intermingled with those of *Parlatoria cinerea* Hadden on citrus in Israel (Gerson 1964). This presented an opportunity to examine the numerical interrelationships between these two closely related diaspidids in the field.

Methods

Mixed populations of *P. pergandii* and *P. cinerea* (both of which infest all above-ground parts of the citrus trees) were sampled in two orange groves, situated about 20 miles apart, along the coastal plain of Israel. At the Ramot Hashavim grove, sampling began in September 1963 and proceeded to June 1966. At the Rehovot grove, the period covered lasted from February 1964 to April 8, 1965, on which date this grove was uprooted. Monthly (during the first year) or bi-monthly (during the rest of the period) sampling consisted of collecting about 20 to 25 small twigs from about 10 trees per grove. Usually only the lowest leaf was examined, and up to five live females collected from each twig. In this manner, 100 live females of *Parlatoria* spp. were obtained, mounted and examined on each date from each one of the two groves. Preliminary studies showed that a sample of 100 live famales gave reliable estimates of population changes. Individual scales were collected at random, since, though the two species may live side by side on the leaves, the positive identification of the respective species according to their scales alone is unreliable. Citrus was the only host-plant of the two diaspidids in the groves.

Results and Discussion

The results obtained during the period of the investigation (Fig. 1) show the existence of definite seasonal trends in the relative abundance of the two species. The populations of *P. cinerea* were larger during winter, whereas those of *P. pergandii* reached their relative peaks in the summer. This held true for both groves sampled, and for the entire period of the study. Such a situation is entirely different from all other interrelationships hitherto reported, whereby one species of scale insects completely displaces the other.

It seems safe to conclude at present that the populations of these two diaspidids have reached a certain degree of equilibrium. It is not, however, possible to infer whether this is only a temporary state of affairs, or if the two populations have already stabilized.

As the two diaspidids apparently infest all above-ground parts of the citrus trees to an equal degree, they may be considered to be the true homologues as to their feeding and settlement requirements. In this respect they differ from the two species of *Aonidiella* discussed. *A. aurantii* infests all above-ground parts of the citrus trees, but *A. citrina* infests only the leaves and fruits (Flanders 1956, DeBach and Sundby 1963).

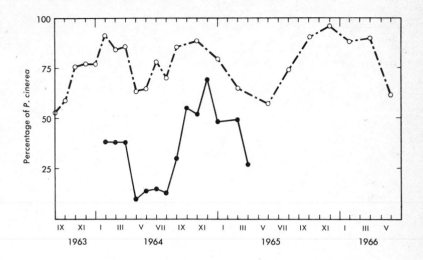

Fig. 1. The relative abundance of *Parlatoria cinerea* Hadden in samples of 100 live females of *Parlatoria* spp. on citrus leaves (○———○ = Ramat Hashavim; ●———● = Rehovot).

During a concurrent investigation (Gerson 1964) it was found that both species of *Parlatoria* are parasitized by the same two hymenopterous species, and preyed upon by various predators. But no clear evidence was found to indicate differential parasite or predator action on these scale insects.

A partial explanation for the observed interrelationships between the two species of *Parlatoria* may be obtained from studying their geographical distribution. *P. pergandii* infests citrus trees almost wherever these are grown, whereas *P. cinerea* was collected, from the same plant-host, mostly in humid tropical regions (Morrison 1939). These differences in distribution suggest that the two species differ somewhat in their relative tolerance to desiccation. In Israel a dry and hot summer follows the cold, wet winter. Thus cyclic, seasonal changes in climatic conditions annually modify the habitat, determine which *Parlatoria* sp. will be dominant, and enable the coexistence of these species. Possibly similar relationships exist between other, closely related species, helping to explain their coexistence in the same ecological niche.

•   •   •

Literature Cited

DeBach, P. 1966. The competitive displacement and coexistence principles. *Ann. Rev. Ent.* **11**: 183–212.

———— and R. A. Sundby. 1963. Competitive displacement between ecological homologues. *Hilgradia* **34**: 105–166.

Flanders, S. E. 1956. Struggle for existence between red and yellow scale. *Calif. Citrog.* **41**: 396–403.

Gerson, U. 1964. *Parlatoria cinerea*, a pest of citrus in Israel. *FAO Pl. Prot. Bull.* **12**: 82–85.

Morrison, H. 1939. Taxonomy of some scale insects of the genus *Parlatoria* encountered in plant quarantine inspection work. *U.S. Dept. of Agr. Misc. Pub.*, No. 344: 34 pp.

Schweig, C. and A. Gruenberg. 1936. The problem of black scale (*Chrysomphalus ficus* Ashm.) in Palestine. *Bull. Ent. Res.* **27**: 677–713.

Cave Adaptation in Amblyopsid Fishes

Thomas L. Poulson

Abstract

The Amblyopsidae show a sequence of adaptation to caves where they have no predators and food is the main limiting factor. The sequence is shown, in order, by the epigean species *Chologaster cornuta*, the troglophile *C. agassizi*, and the three troglobites *Typhlichthys subterraneus*, *Amblyopsis spelaea*, and *A. rosae*. Eye and pigment degeneration are a time index for length of isolation in caves. Extent of degeneration is correlated with extent of cave adaptation in amblyopsids and other cave fish, with the modifying influence of food supply, number of predators, and sensory endowment of the ancestral species.

In the Amblyopsidae the epigean species is preadapted to caves by having small eyes, being nocturnal, and having sensory receptors which allow feeding and orientation in an aphotic environment. However, it cannot survive in an aphotic environment. Its troglophilic relative can survive in an aphotic environment.

As cave adaptation progresses eyes become reduced and degenerate and pigment may be lost. At first, eye and optic lobe variance are high but variance decreases as the effects of allometry, accumulation of mutations under relaxed selection, and ontogenetic degeneration become stabilized.

Olfactory receptors, neuromast receptors, tactile receptors, and equilibrium receptors and their brain centers become more hypertrophied as cave adaptation increases. Capacity to integrate sensory information, as reflected by ability to detect prey and avoid obstacles or remember their position, also increases. The head becomes larger; fins become longer, and neuromasts more exposed.

Absolute growth rate decreases with increasing cave adaptation. Lower developmental rates are related to larger and fewer eggs. As number of eggs decreases so does rate of population growth. Lower rate of population growth is also related to increasing age at first reproduction and increasing longevity. These changes and irregular reproduction by few of the potentially breeding fish cause a shift of population structure toward adults in the more cave adapted species.

Metabolic rates and intensity of reaction to disturbing stimuli decrease with increasing cave adaptation. This does not involve a sacrifice of activity since swimming frequency and efficiency are higher in the more specialized species.

• • •

Introduction

The striking convergence shown by cave animals in eye degeneration and pigment reduction is well known but the biology of cave animals has rarely been studied. Excellent studies of eye structure and pigmentation by Eigenmann (1909) show that the species of amblyopsid fish comprise a morphological series including a non-cave (epigean) form with eyes and pigment, a facultative cave form (troglophile) with reduced eyes and pigment, and

Reprinted by permission of the author and publisher from *The American Midland Naturalist* **70**: 257–290, 1963.

several obligate cave forms (troglobites) with degenerate eyes and no pigment. The next major study of the Amblyopsidae was of distribution and variation, and resulted in a revision of the family (Woods and Inger, 1957).

The present study of the Amblyopsidae shows that the five species are differentially adapted to cave life. In order of increasing eye degeneration and pigment loss the five species of amblyopsids are the epigean *Chologaster cornuta* Agassiz, the troglophile *Chologaster agassizi* Putnam, and the troglobites *Typhlichthys subterraneus* Girard, *Amblyopsis spelaea* DeKay, and *Amblyopsis rosae* (Eigenmann). The aspects of adaptation reported here are brain and sense organ morphology, absolute growth rate, metabolic rate, feeding and obstacle avoidance behavior, and some aspects of ecology and life history. These aspects of amblyopsid biology show a pattern of adaptation to cave life which parallels eye degeneration and pigment loss.

•   •   •

Discussion

Adaptive Traits

The increase in relative head size with increased cave adaptation is associated with branchial incubation and increased importance of neuromasts and tactile receptors. The longer pectoral and caudal fins of the troglobites enable more efficient swimming which conserves energy but a more important advantage is the reduction of interference "noise" for neuromast receptors. Increased thrust per stroke provides a longer glide period during which there is no "noise." The 10–20 mm difference between the distance that a prey causes cupular movement in a stationary fish and the distance at which a gliding fish orients toward the same prey shows the advantage of decreased "noise." Water movement by prey disturbs the flow pattern around the gliding fish's head thus modifying the background pattern of neuromast sensory activity. In a stream *Amblyopsis* is particularly sensitive to changes in flow pattern and will slow to half its speed when obstacles are 250–400 mm ahead and will start to avoid them at 100–150 mm.

Because of differences in neuromasts . . . *Typhlichthys* is more sensitive than *Amblyopsis* to general water movement but less sensitive to the direction from which movement comes. The neuromast arrangement of *Typhlichthys* is advantageous to an inactive fish in detecting copepod prey in a quiet water habitat and that of *Amblyopsis* is advantageous to a more active fish in detecting larger prey in a stream habitat.

In an artificial stream *A. spelaea* is eight times and *A. rosae*, one and a half times as rheotactic as *Typhlichthys*. *Typhlichthys* swims in quiet water, usually at the substrate or with the top of its head touching and parallel to surfaces. Both *Amblyopsis* species often swim in midwater and show positive rheotaxis in currents of 2–7 cm/sec without tactile reference though *A. rosae* tends to remain just over or among rocks. While swimming upstream over rocks or next to obstacles both *Amblyopsis* species slow down to half their swimming velocity in open water.

After swimming upstream both *Amblyopsis* species often swim to the surface and drift downstream without tactile reference. While moving passively downstream, they often turn somersaults and drift at various angles, not showing orientation again until they contact some obstacle or reach their initial starting point. This behavior is explained by interaction of lateral line, semicircular canal and otolith sensory input in absence of tactile reference. Some *Amblyopsis* in nature often swim upstream foraging and drift downstream in the same area for days, indicating a spatial memory and suggesting a home range.

The better spatial memory of *Amblyopsis* as compared to *Typhlichthys* or *C. agassizi* is due to lesser dependence on thigmotaxis and is related to greater cerebellum and telencephalon development. Increase in telencephalon size may also be related to the decrease in excitability shown by troglobite amblyopsids, since there is evidence that the teleost telencephalon is associated with inhibition of behavioral patterns (Healy, 1957).

Eyes and Pigment

The eyes of *C. cornuta* probably form images but if there were selection for image formation the ciliary muscles of *C. agassizi* would be present and there would be lower variance of eye and optic lobe size. *C. agassizi* depends on its smaller eyes only for discrimination of light intensity. Cave *C. agassizi* show reduced absolute growth rate because of poor food supply so much of the further eye and pigment reduction in the cave *C. agassizi* can be accounted for by the high positive allometry of these characters (see Poulson, 1961). Contrary to the general case that b for a character is constant intraspecifically (Martin, 1949), b for pigmented melanophores and eyes is lower than for spring *C. agassizi* (Poulson, 1961). Also, bipolar cells and spongioblasts of the retina are reduced (Eigenmann, 1909), and goblet cells in the epithelium over the eye make the eye less sensitive to differences in light intensity. This indicates that there is already some accumulation of loss mutations with reduction of selection pressure. Allometry and mutation are reflected by the high variance for eye and optic lobe seen even in a partially epigean population of *C. agassizi*. The variance for the eyes of *Typhlichthys* is still higher suggesting that both accumulation of loss mutations and allometry are still operating. *A. spelaea* shows less variance possibly because loss mutations are starting to balance back mutations and pleiotropic effects on eyes. Eigenmann's studies of eye embryology (1909) show that allometry is responsible for much of the eye degeneration of *A. spelaea* subsequent to the stage in early development when histogenesis is arrested. The eyes of *A. rosae* are much more degenerate than those of *A. spelaea* (Eigenmann, 1909). The effects of allometry and loss mutation seem to be stabilized and balanced with back mutation and pleiotropic effects in *A. rosae* because the variance is even less than for *C. cornuta* and the *b*'s for eye and optic lobe size are very low.

Further evidence for the role of acumulation of loss mutations with reduced selection pressure is the difficulty of predicting the order in which parts of the eye will be affected and the rate at which degeneration of given parts proceeds. All evidence, including overall eye degeneration, indicates that *Typhlichthys* has not been in caves as long as *A. splaea*, but in some respects its eyes are more degenerate. *A. spelaea* has a *b* of 0.43 for eyes, loses its lens as an embryo, has a retina with pigment but no outer reticular layer, and has some eye muscles, whereas some *Typhlichthys* have a *b* of 0.25 for eyes, do not lose the lens, have a retina with an outer reticular layer but no pigment, and have no eye muscles (Eigenmann, 1909).

Growth Rates and Adaptation

Selection for morphological adaptation in caves appears to have acted largely through changes of absolute and relative growth rates. A generally lowered absolute growth rate and allometry accounts for differences in body proportions in *C. cornuta* populations and some of the change in body proportions which *C. agassizi* shows in caves. Changes in *b* account for more of the changes. Together lower growth rate and higher *b*'s acount for much of the increase in head size, cerebellum size, semicircular canal and otolith size, neuromast number and fin length which *Typhlichthys* shows. However, only early growth rate decreases further with further increase in cave adaptation and *b*'s increase only slightly so the morphological changes shown by the two species of *Amblyopsis* must be due to other factors in addition to allometry. With lower developmental rates and larger yolked eggs, the more specialized troglobites are larger at hatching and end of yolk absorption and smaller at completion of vent migration. This neoteny and larger size at growth inflections account for further increases in head, fin, cerebellum, and telencephalon size and increases in neuromast exposure. Further hypertrophy of other sense organs and integrative centers is probably directly due to selection and pleiotropy.

General Discussion

Most previous studies of cave fish deal with explanations of eye degeneration and pigment loss (Eigenmann, 1909; Hubbs, 1938). The few previous interpretations of cave adaptation based on biology differ markedly (Breder, 1953; Heuts, 1953; Marshall and Thines, 1958) because the studies are on single species exemplifying different lengths of isolation in caves where different factors are limiting. In this study I have based interpretations of cave adaptation on the Amblyopsidae which includes an epigean species, a troglophile species, and three troglobite species which, on the basis of all evidence, have been in caves for increasing lengths of time. Food scarcity and lack of predators are the main factors which have affected cave adaptation in the Amblyopsidae. Study of these fish has shown a sequence of cave adaptation which is outlined here and, according to my evaluation of fragmentary evidence, is exemplified by the few cave fish about which biology is known (the Mexican cave characins, *Anoptichthys*; Breder 1943, Rasquin 1947, Rasquin and Rosenbloom 1954, and see Poulson 1963: the Brazilian cave catfish, *Pimelodella kronei*; Pavan 1946: the Congo cave barb, *Caecobarbus geertsi*; Heuts 1951, Thines 1955, and see Poulson 1963: The Cuban cave brotulids, *Stygicola* and *Lucifuga*; Eigenmann 1909: The Iraq cave cyprinid, *Typhlogarra widdowsoni*; Marshall and Thines 1958: and the Amblyopsidae). The sequence is arbitrarily divided into three stages with subdivisions in each. Changes first discussed under one subdivision continue subsequently, and to a certain extent changes within each stage are concurrent. The applicability of this sequence to cave fauna other than fish is discussed elsewhere (Poulson, 1963).

First Stages

Preadaptation

In some sense preadaptation was probably a requisite to cave adaptation in all troglobites. Preadaptation of the epigean ancestor might include presence of hypertrophied taste, olfactory, tactile or lateral line systems allowing feeding and orientation in a cave environment; presence of negative phototaxis, negative thermotaxis, or positive rheotaxis favoring entry into a cave environment; or presence of tendencies toward eye and pigment mutations surviving only in a cave environment. Among amblyopsids *Chologaster cornuta* is preadapted in all these aspects. *Astyanax mexicanus*, the ancestor of *Anoptichthys*, is preadapted in the second and third aspects and if placed in an aphotic situation, will assume the substrate circling-feeding behavior typical of *Anoptichthys*. *Pimelodella transitoria*, the ancestor of *P. kronei*, and *Garra rufa*, an epigean relative of *Typhlogarra*, are preadapted by having large numbers of taste receptors and negative phototaxis.

Endocrine Adjustment

Fish must adapt to aphotic conditions endocrinologically before they can survive in caves. *Astyanax mexicanus* though preadapted by behavior will, when placed in the dark, develop endocrine imbalance leading to tissue hyperplasia and skeletal deformities and pituitary degeneration leading to atrophy of gonadal, thyroid, and interrenal tissue. Even *Chologaster cornuta*, preadapted by behavior, sense organs, and eye reduction will, when placed in the dark, develop vertebral deformities, emaciation, and uncoordinated swimming after 3 to 4 months and will die after 4 to 5 months. *C. agassizi* is adjusted endocrinologically because spring populations live well in permanent darkness in the laboratory.

Increased Eye and Pigment Variance

Longer fins, larger head, and reduction of eyes and pigment are effects of allometry due to reduced absolute growth rates. The fact that cave *C. agassizi* have less fat and lower weight per unit length than spring *C. agassizi* indicates that the reduced growth rate is due to poor food supply. Relaxed selection allows accumulation of eye and pigment mutations and thus adds further to their high variance. High eye and pigment variability is also seen in *Anoptichthys jordani* and *Pimelodella kronei*. In *A. jordani,* there appears to be better integration of sensory information used in feeding and orientation at the time when sense organ number is increasing but before brain centers for sense organs hypertrophy. *C. agassizi* shows such hypertrophy but *Anoptichthys* does not. The condition shown by *A. hubbsi* and *A. antrobius* suggests that there will be further eye and pigment degeneration and adaptation but little further adaptation in *A. jordani,* because food is not limiting.

Second Stages

Lowered Growth and Metabolic Rates

Greater fat deposits and increased weight per unit length are consistent with lower growth rate and lower active and standard metabolic rates being selected by low food supply. Sensory receptors continue to increase in number, and their brain centers become markedly hypertrophied. Larger heads, longer fins, and more exposed sensory receptors reflect both allometry, which results from higher relative and lower absolute growth rates, and neotenic trends. Eyes and pigment are much reduced and still show high variance but melanin may still be induced by prolonged exposure to light. This level of adaptation is exemplified by some populations of *Typhlichthys* and *Caecobarbus* and, as regards eyes and pigment, by *Anoptichthys hubbsi* and *A. antrobius*.

Change in Developmental Rate
and Population Structure

The changes already discussed continue and adjustments of population growth are selected in a food-poor environment. Longevity increases and population structure shifts toward adults. This shift is not common to all populations of a species since it is due to lack of reproduction in those years when food supply is low and population density is high. *Caecobarbus,* *Typhlichthys,* and possibly *Stygicola* and *Lucifuga* show this phenomenon.

Parental care is also selected. There is decreased fecundity and increased egg size and developmental rate which results in larger free swimming fry.

This is accompanied by branchial incubation in amblyopsids and ovoviviparity in *Stygicola* and *Lucifuga*.

Pigment is reduced further and eye degeneration is enhanced by earlier cessation of differentiation in the embryo. However, pigment can still be induced by light and there is little ontogenetic degeneration of eyes once their differentiation has stopped.

Lower Routine Metabolic Rate

Decreased reaction to disturbing stimuli reflected by lower routine metabolic rate is the most important of the next changes. Sensory receptors and their brain centers continue to hypertrophy. Better central nervous system integration is shown by better ability to avoid obstacles and detect food. *Typhlichthys* shows these changes and *Caecobarbus* shows some of them. *Caecobarbus* is still very excitable and locates food slowly despite some hypertrophy of sensory receptors.

Third Stages

Population Regulation

There are further shifts of population structure toward adults in all habitats. Small proportions of the potentially breeding females spawn in those years when population density is low. This and further increases in longevity and age at first reproduction and further decrease in fecundity results in much lower rates of population growth. Absolute growth, developmental and standard and active metabolic rates continue to decrease and there is an increase in neotenic tendencies. *Amblyopsis spelaea* exemplifies these and the next series of changes.

Decreased Eye and Pigment Variance

Ontogenetic eye degeneration adds to eye and pigment variance and pigment can no longer be induced by light, and overall eye and pigment variance decreases. Reaction to disturbing stimuli is still lower and routine metabolic rate is very low. However more frequent swimming and greater swimming efficiency allow the fish to forage more extensively. There are gaps in our knowledge of the biology of *Typhlogarra*, but it is tentatively assigned to this level of cave adaptation because of extreme eye degeneration and refractoriness to disturbing stimuli.

Better Integration of Sensory Information

Sense organs and their brain centers show no further hypertrophy and eyes and pigment show very low variance. However, better central nervous system integration of sensory information is indicated by increased ability to detect obstacles and food and to remember positions of obstacles. Standard, active, and routine metabolic rates and rate of population growth are still decreasing. Further neotenic trends are indicated by relatively longer fins, larger heads, and greater exposure of sense organs. *Amblyopsis rosae* exemplifies these changes. No known cave fish shows further changes but it might be predicted that further changes would extend those outlined here and extend to those seen in bathypelagic fish which are in a much older and more food-poor habitat (Poulson, 1963).

Conclusions

There is considerable convergence in cave adaptation. The extent of eye and pigment degeneration reflects length of isolation in caves because most of the degeneration results from accumulation of mutations with relaxed selection. Using the time scale provided by knowledge of eye and pigment degeneration I believe it is possible to predict the stage of cave adaptation attained if the extent of food scarcity, the number of predators, and the sensory endowment of the ancestral species or group is known. It is mainly these last factors which account for the supposed (Breder, 1953; Marshall and Thines, 1958; and Thines, 1955) diversity of adaptation in cave fish. For example, if food is not limiting, a fish may be no more adapted than the latter part of Stage I even if eyes and pigment are degenerate (e.g., *Anoptichthys jordani*). Also, if the ancestral form is well endowed with taste receptors and the organic food is not too scarce a fish may be in Stage I for sense organs and their brain centers and yet have extremely degenerate eyes (e.g., *Typhlogarra*). In most cases, however, food is limiting and the ancestral form is only moderately endowed with sense organs so stage of adaptation correlates closely with extent of eye and pigment degeneration (e.g., the Amblyopsidae, *Caecobarbus*, *Anoptichthys hubbsi* and *A. antrobius*, *Pimelodella kronei*, and *Stygicola* and *Lucifuga*).

• • •

References

American Public Health Association. 1955. *Standard Methods for the Examination of Water and Sewage*. New York. 10th ed. 522 p.

Anderson, R. O. 1959. The influence of season and temperature on growth of the Bluegill, *Lepomis machrochirus*. Ph. D. dissert., Univ. Mich., 133 p.

Basu, S. P. 1959. Active respiration of fish in relation to ambient concentrations of oxygen and carbon dioxide. J. Fish. Res. Bd. Canada **16**: 175–212.

Breder, C. M. Jr. 1943. Problems in the behavior and evolution of a species of blind cave fish. Trans. N. Y. Acad. Sci., Ser. II **5**: 168–176.

——— 1953. Cave fish evolution. *Evolution* 7: 179–180.

Brett, J. R., M. Hollands and D. F. Alderdice. 1958. The effect of temperature on the cruising speed of young sockeye and coho salmon. *J. Fish. Res. Bd. Canada* **15**: 587–605.

Cole, L. C. 1954. The population consequences of life history phenomena. *Quart. Rev. Biol.* **29**: 103–137.

Eigenmann, C. H. 1909. Cave vertebrates of America, a study in degenerative evolution. *Carn. Inst. Wash. Publ.* **104**: 1–241.

Evans, F. C. and F. E. Smith. 1952. The intrinsic rate of natural increase for the Human Louse, *Pediculus humanus*. *Am. Nat.* **86**: 299–310.

Fry, F. E. J. 1957. Aquatic respiration of fish, p. 1–63. In M. E. Brown, ed. *Physiology of Fishes*. Academic Press. Vol. 1, New York.

––––– and J. S. Hart. 1948. The relation of temperature to oxygen consumption in the goldfish. *Biol. Bull.* **94**: 66–77.

Graham, J. M. 1954. Some effects of temperature and oxygen pressure on the metabolism and activity of the Speckled Trout, *Salvelinus fontinalis*. *Canadian J. Res.* D, **27**: 270–288.

Hawes, R. S. 1939. The flood factor in the ecology of caves. *J. Animal Ecol.* **8**: 1–5.

Healy, E. G. 1957. The nervous system, p. 1–119. In M. E. Brown, ed., *Physiology of Fishes*. Academic Press, New York. Vol. 2.

Heuts, M. J. 1951. Ecology, variation and adaptation of the blind African cave fish, *Caecobarbus geertsi*. *Ann. Soc. Roy. Zool. Belg.* **82**: 155–230.

––––– 1953. Regressive evolution in cave animals, p. 290–309. In *Sympos. Soc. Exper. Biol.*, VII. Academic Press, New York.

Hoar, W. S. 1957. Endocrine organs, p. 245–285. In M. E. Brown, ed., *Physiology of Fishes*. Academic Press, New York. Vol. 1.

Hubbs, C. L. 1938. Fishes from the caves of Yucatan. *Carn. Inst. Wash. Publ.* **491**: 261–295.

Jeannel, R. 1943. *Les Fossiles Vivants des Cavernes*. Avenir de la Science, N. S., I. Gallimard, Paris. 321 p.

Job, S. V. 1955. The oxygen consumption of *Salvelinus fontinalis*. *Univ. Toronto Studies, Biol. Ser.* 61, *Publ. Ontario Fish. Res. Lab.* **73**: 1–39.

John, K. R. 1957. Observations on the behavior of blind and blinded fishes. *Copeia* **1957**: 123–132.

Keys, A. B. 1930. The measure of the respiratory exchange of aquatic animals. *Biol. Bull.* **59**: 187–198.

Marshall, N. B. and G. L. Thines. 1958. Studies of the brain, sense organs and light sensitivity of a blind cave fish (*Typhlogarra widdowsoni*) from Iraq. *Proc. Zool. Soc. Lond.* **131**: 441–456.

Martin, W. R. 1949. The mechanisms of environmental control of body form in fishes. *Univ. Toronto Studies, Biol. Ser.* **58**, *Publ. Ontario Fish. Res. Lab.* **70**: 1–72.

Pavan, C. 1946. Observations and experiments on the cave fish *Pimelodella kronei* and its relatives. *Am. Nat.* **80**: 343–361.

Poulson, T. L. 1961. Cave adaptation in amblyopsid fishes. Ph. D. dissert., U. Mich., Mic. 61–2787, U. Microfilms, Ann Arbor.

––––– 1964. Cave adaptation. In D. B. Dill, ed., *Handbook of Physiology, Adaptation to the Environment*, American Physiological Society: 749–771.

Rasquin, P. 1947. Progressive pigmentary regression in fishes associated with cave environments. *Zoologica* **32**: 35–42.

––––– and L. Rosenbloom. 1954. Endocrine imbalance and tissue hyperplasia in teleosts maintained in darkness. *Bull. Am. Mus. Nat. Hist.* **104**: 359–426.

Scott, W. 1909. An ecological study of the plankton of Shawnee Cave. *Biol. Bull.* **17**: 386–402.

Smith, F. E. 1954. Quantitative aspects of population growth, p. 277–294. In E. J. Boell, ed., *Dynamics of Growth Processes*. Princeton Univ. Press, Princeton.

Swift, D. R. 1959. Seasonal variation in the activity of the thyroid gland of yearling Brown Trout, *Salmo trutta. J. Expt. Biol.* **36**: 120–125.

Thines, G. 1955. Les poissons aveugles (I): origine, taxonomie, répartition géographique, comportement. *Ann. Soc. Roy. Zool. Belg.* **86**: 1–128.

Weise, J. G. 1957. The spring cavefish, *Chologaster papilliferus*, in Illinois. *Ecology* **38**: 196–204.

Wells, N. A. 1932. The importance of the time element in the determination of the respiratory metabolism in fishes. *Proc. Natl. Acad. Sci. (U.S.)* **18**: 580–585.

——— 1935. Variation in the respiratory metabolism of the Pacific Killifish, *Fundulus parvipinnis*, due to size, season, and continued constant temperature. *Physiol. Zool.* **8**: 318–335.

Wohlschlag, D. E. and R. O. Juliano. 1959. Seasonal changes in Bluegill metabolism. *Limnol. and Oceanog.* **4**: 195–209.

Woods, L. P. and R. F. Inger. 1957. The cave, spring, and swamp fishes of the family Amblyopsidae of central and eastern United States. *Am. Midl. Nat.* **58**: 232–256.

Population Studies on Lead-Tolerant
Agrostis tenuis

D. Jowett

Lead mines, mostly disused, are a common feature of the landscape of Central and North Wales. Usually they consist of heaps of mine spoil together with flat expanses of ground ore from which the bulk of the lead has been extracted. Both the thin soil cover over the mine spoil and the spent ore frequently contain toxic amounts of lead. This is particularly true of ore grindings produced prior to about 1925, when extraction processes became more efficient. The sites fall into two main groups—the acidic in Central Wales and Snowdonia, and the calcareous in Flintshire. The present paper is concerned with the former. On the most toxic sites the vegetation is sparse and is almost a pure stand of *Agrostis tenuis*. Where the soil is less toxic other species occur, but *A. tenuis* still provides most of the soil cover. Species such as *Thlaspi alpestre* and *Minuartia verna*, traditionally associated with metal-rich soils, only occur when the pH is higher. Elsewhere in the British Isles on acidic sites, *Festuca ovina* is more common on lead mines than *A. tenuis* (Wilkins, 1957). The reason for this is not known.

A. tenuis occurring on Goginan mine in Cardiganshire has been described as lead tolerant by Bradshaw (1952), and several populations tolerant of either copper, nickel, or lead (but never more than one metal) have been described by Jowett (1958). The present paper carries the investigation further and compares the characteristics of lead-tolerant populations with those occupying more normal habitats.

In addition to the intrinsic interest of the study of the evolutionary response of a species to a man-made hazard, this situation is relevant to general considerations of population dynamics. The sites vary in size, but are often quite small, and are always sharply delineated from the surrounding vegetation. Furthermore, we know approximately when the sites first became available to plant colonization. Lead was certainly produced in quantity in Flintshire in Roman times, but there is little or no evidence of this in Cardiganshire, the main area with which this study is concerned. The Pax Romana was not very effective in the Cardiganshire area, and it would seem unlikely that lead-contaminated areas were available for plant colonization before the 16th century. From the data to be presented we can speculate on the spatial and temporal scales on which population differentiation occurs.

• • •

Conclusions

The data clearly indicate that small populations of *A. tenuis* on small areas of land can develop, by selection, a distinct character adapting them

Reprinted by permission of the author and publisher from *Evolution* **18**: 70–81, 1964.

to their particular site. Conditions on these sites include the presence of lead in toxic quantities to which the populations have developed tolerance. It appears that lead mine populations have been able to exploit the whole pool of variability locally available in the species. We can say with certainty that small-scale variations in habitat do not exclude the development of distinct populations. This is direct confirmation of Bradshaw's (1954, 1959) conclusions.

Edaphic ecotypes of the type described may be common, although they require special techniques for their description. Furthermore, such ecotypes may require only a short time for their development. In strongly perennial species rapid evolution is possible without much isolation if selection is sufficiently strong. This study indicates that it may be very strong on lead mines, particularly for tolerance of lead. But the populations also show adaptation to a wide range of characters for which selection may be thought to be much less severe, e.g., early flowering.

Ford (1956) has suggested that the subdivision of a population into small isolated or semi-isolated units promotes its rapid evolution because each group can then be adjusted to the particular ecology of its habitat. The work described here indicates that in a perennial plant species a subunit occupying an area 50 yards across can be adjusted to the particular ecology of its habitat, and even this does not represent a proved lower limit. It seems probable that the distance necessary in plants to permit sufficient reproductive isolation to allow the emergence of distinct types has in the past been overestimated.

Summary

1. Populations of *A. tenuis* growing on disused lead mines are shown to be generally lead tolerant when compared with populations from normal habitats.

2. There is variation in the degree of tolerance possessed by genotypes on particular mines.

3. Plants of the lead mine populations are smaller for a range of morphological characters, lower yielding than normal populations, and earlier flowering. The adaptive significance of these characters is discussed.

4. Comparison of a mine and normal population in sand culture shows that the mine population is adapted to the low levels of calcium and phosphate found in lead mine soils.

5. Sites only 50 yards across are quite capable of supporting distinct populations adapted to the site characteristics. It is suggested that such adapted populations have arisen during the last two or three hundred years at the most.

Literature Cited

Bradshaw, A. D. 1952. Populations of *Agrostis tenuis* resistant to lead and zinc poisoning. *Nature* **169**: 1098.

────── 1954. Local population differences in *Agrostis tenuis*. Proc. IXth Int. Cong. Genetics. *Caryologia*, vol. suppl., 1026–1028.

────── 1959. Population differentiation in *Agrostis tenuis*. I. Morphological differentiation. *New Phytol.* **58**: 208–227.

────── R. W. Lodge, D. Jowett, and M. J. Chadwick. 1958. Experimental investigations into the mineral nutrition of several grass species. I. Calcium level. *J. Ecol.* **46**: 749–757.

──────, ──────, ──────, and ──────. 1960a. Experimental investigations into the mineral nutrition of several grass species. II. Calcium and pH. *J. Ecol.* **48**: 143–150.

──────, ──────, M. J. Chadwick, D. Jowett, and R. W. Snaydon. 1960b. Experimental investigations into the mineral nutrition of several grass species. III. Calcium and phosphorus. *J. Ecol.* **48**: 631–638.

────── and R. W. Snaydon. 1959. Population differentiation within plant species in response to soil factors. *Nature* **183**: 129–130.

Cooper, J. P. 1959. Selection and population structure in Lolium. III. Selection for date of ear emergence. *Heredity* **13**: 461–480.

Ford, E. B. 1956. Rapid evolution and the conditions which make it possible. *Cold Spring Harbor Symp.* **20**: 230–238.

Gregor, J. W. 1944. The ecotype. *Biol. Rev.* **19**: 20–30.

──────, V. McM. Davey, and J. M. S. Lang. 1936. Experimental taxonomy. I. Experimental garden techniques in relation to the recognition of the small taxonomic units. *New Phytol.* **35**: 323–350.

Griffiths, D. J. 1950. The liability of seed crops of perennial rye-grass to contamination by wind-borne pollen. *J. Agri. Sci.* **40**: 19.

Harberd, D. J. 1956. Correlated characters in population studies. *New Phytol.* **55**: 154–163.

────── 1958. A spurious significance in genecological trials. *Nature* **181**: 138.

Jowett, D. 1958. Populations of *Agrostis* spp. tolerant of heavy metals. *Nature* **182**: 816–817.

────── 1959. Genecology of heavy metal tolerance in *Agrostis*. Ph. D. Thesis, University of Wales.

Morley, F. H. W. 1959. Natural selection in relation to ecotype and racial differentiation in plants. *Cold Spring Harbor Symp.* **24**: 47–56.

Riley, R. 1956. The influence of the breeding system on the genecology of *Thlaspi alpestre*. *New Phytol.* **55**: 319–330.

Sandell, E. B. 1950. *Colorimetric Determination of Traces of Metals*. Interscience, New York, 673 p.

Snaydon, R. W., and A. D. Bradshaw. 1961. Differential response to calcium within *Festuca ovina*. *New Phytol.* **60**: 219–234.

Thoday, J. M., and J. B. Gibson. 1962. Isolation by disruptive selection. *Nature* **193**: 1164–1166.

Wilkins, D. W. 1957. A technique for the measurement of lead tolerance in plants. *Nature* **180**: 37–38.

Color Change and the Ecology of the Marine Isopod *Idothea* (*Pentidotea*) *montereyensis* Maloney, 1933

Welton L. Lee

Abstract

The isopod *Idothea montereyensis* lives on marine plants in the rocky intertidal zone on the west coast of North America. It occurs in red, green and brownish color varieties which usually match the color of the plant on which the isopod is found, and individuals are capable of undergoing color change when transferred to plants of another color.

A population of *Idothea montereyensis* occurs on the eelgrass *Phyllospadix scouleri* which forms large beds at about the 0.0 tidal level; these animals are subjected to wave action which may be severe during the winter. Another population occurs inshore of the *Phyllospadix* on various species of red algae which grow in the more protected deeper pools and channels.

During the year, when large numbers of young are released, there is a massive exchange of individuals between the *Phyllospadix* and the red algal populations. Young which cannot hold on in the exposed *Phyllospadix* beds are swept in to the inshore red algae, while, presumably as a result of population pressure, the adult animals on inshore red algae move out to the *Phyllospadix* beds. The result of these major population exchanges is clearly advantageous. Young which cannot hold on to the *Phyllospadix* are provided with a protected habitat for development and growth on the inshore red algae, whereas the adults moving to the *Phyllospadix* are provided with ample space and food in a region where they are not competing strongly with their own young for these things. It is the middle-sized and larger animals which survive through the winter on *Phyllospadix;* the summer young grow and develop in the protected inshore areas.

The ability to change color may allow the animals to utilize for food and substrate a larger quantity and variety of intertidal plants, with greater safety from predators, than would be possible without color change. It may provide camouflage to animals within a relatively short time after the occurrence of highly advantageous shifts in habitat.

* * *

Conclusions

Figure 1 summarizes the yearly cycle of events occurring in and between the two populations of *I. montereyensis*. Significant among the results of this study is the observation that the two populations exchange considerable numbers of individuals at specific times during the year. Most notable are the large numbers of newly released young which move from the *Phyllospadix* beds to the red algae in the summer, and the movement of medium

Reprinted by permission of the author and publisher from *Ecology* **47**: 930–941, 1966.

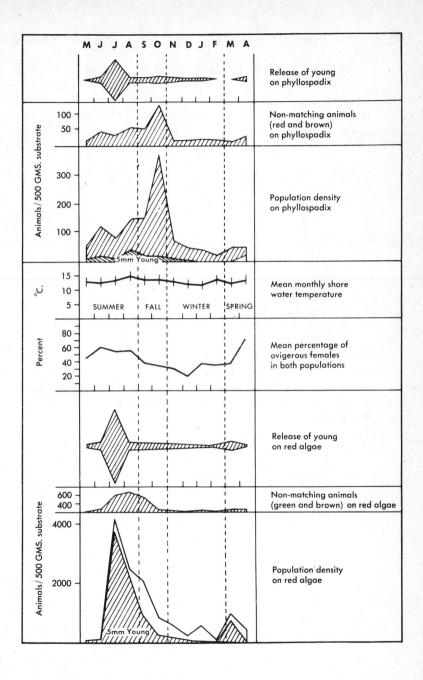

Fig. 1. A summary of the yearly cycle of events occurring in and between the two populations of *Idothea montereyensis*.

and large sized animals from the red algae to *Phyllospadix* from June through October.

In general, the outer, more exposed *Phyllospadix* beds provide a vastly greater total amount of available food and substrate than the inshore red algae. A disadvantage of this area, however, is its greater exposure to damaging winter storms and to fairly turbulent conditions even at other seasons. The red algae of the protected pools and channels closer to shore, though of smaller total biomass, provide a much better protected habitat and food supply.

The probable causes for the movement of animals to alternate substrates appear different in the two populations. In the isopod population on red algae the medium and larger sized animals emigrate actively in response to some factor related to population density and/or the presence of huge numbers of small juveniles. On *Phyllospadix*, however, the loss of animals to the inshore red algae is largely restricted to individuals of the smallest size classes. This seems to be due to the relatively poor ability of these younger animals to hold on to the eelgrass in turbulent water. Both the inward movement of small green animals and the outward movement of large red animals occur at, or shortly after, the summer breeding season, when the release of young is highest on *Phyllospadix* and the population density is highest on red algae.

The result of these major exchanges is advantageous to both populations. Young which can not hold on in the exposed *Phyllospadix* areas are provided with a protected habitat for development and growth on the inshore red algae. The adults moving to *Phyllospadix* have ample space and food in an area where they would not have to compete strongly with their own young for these things. These larger animals survive through the winter on *Phyllospadix*, whereas the summer young, which cannot survive here are allowed to grow and develop in the protected inshore areas.

If color change in this species acts as a protective adaptation against predation by intertidal fishes, as has been suggested, then the exchanges between populations might be viewed as allowing the animals to utilize for food and substrate a much larger quantity and variety of intertidal plants, with greater safety from predators, than would be possible without color change.

• • •

Literature Cited

Bauer, V. 1905. Über einen objectiven Nachweis des Simultankontrastes bei Tieren. *Centralbl. Physiol.* **19**: 453–462.

Fingerman, M. 1963. *The Control of Chromatophores*. International series of monographs on pure and applied biology. Macmillan Co., New York. 184 p.

Johnston, R. 1954. The summer food of some intertidal fishes of Monterey County, California. *Calif. Fish and Game* **40**(1): 65–68.

Kjennerund, J. 1950. Ecological observations on *Idothea neglecta*. *Univ. Bergen Arb. Naturv. R.* **7**: 1–47.

Koepcke, H. 1948. Über das Zeichnungsmuster einiger Idotea-Arten (Isopoda). *Zool. Jahrb. Jena (Allg. Zool.)* **61**: 413–460.

Lee, W. L. 1965. Pigments and color change, and their role in the ecology of natural populations of the marine isopod *Idothea montereyensis* Maloney. Ph. D. Thesis. Stanford University.

―――― 1966. Pigmentation of the marine isopod *Idothea montereyensis*. *Comp. Biochem. Physiol.* **18**: 17–36.

Lonnberg, E. and Hellstrom, H. 1931. Zur Kenntnis der Carotenoide bei marinen Evertebraten. *Ark. Zool.* **23**: 1–74.

Matzdorff, C. 1882. Ueber die Färbung von *Idothea tricuspidata*. *Zeit. Naturv.* **16** (N.F.9): 1–58.

Menzies, R. 1950. The taxonomy, ecology and distribution of northern California isopods of the genus *Idothea* with the description of a new species. *Wasmann J. Biol.* **8**(2): 155–195.

Nagano, T. 1949. Physiological studies on the pigmentary system of Crustacea. III. The color change of an isopod *Ligia exotica*. *Sci. Repts. Tohoku Univ., 4th Ser. (Biology)* **18**: 167–172.

Naylor, E. 1955a. The comparative external morphology and revised taxonomy of the British species of *Idotea*. *J. Mar. Biol. Assoc. U.K.* **34**: 467–493.

―――― 1955b. The diet and feeding mechanism of *Idotea*. *J. Mar. Biol. Assoc. U.K.* **34**: 347–355.

―――― 1955c. The life cycle of *Idotea emarginata*. *J. Animal Ecol.* **24**: 270–281.

Oguro, C. 1959. On the physiology of melanophores in the marine isopod, *Idotea japonica*. I. *Endrocrinologia Japonica* **6**(4): 246–252.

―――― 1962. On the physiology of melanophores of the marine isopod, *Idotea japonica*. III. The role of the eyes in background response. *Crustaceana* **4**(2): 6–92.

Pieron, H. 1913. Le mécanisme de l'adaptation chromatique et la livrée nocturne de l'*Idotea tricuspidata*. *C.R. Acad. Sci. Paris.* **157**: 451–453.

Remane, A. 1931. Farbwechsel, Farbrassen und Farbanpassung bei der Meeresassel, *Idothea tricuspidata*. *Verhandl. Deutsch. Zool. Gesell.* **34**: 109–114.

Richardson, H. 1905. Monograph on the isopods of North America. *Bull. U.S. Nat. Mus.* No. 54.

Wilby, G. 1937. The lingcod *Ophidion elongatus* Gerard. *Biol. Bd. Can. Bull.* **34**: 24 p.

Reflections on the Development of Pollination Systems in African *Proteaceae*

Knut Faegri

. . .

Unfortunately, little is known about the pollination of *Proteaceae*, but a few points are known. Even to the most casual observer ornithophily is obvious, and already in the more primitive anthocladia of *Mimetes* the ornithophilous syndrome is clear: the small lateral inflorescences form brush blossoms of a very regular type. Bird visits have been recorded by Marloth (1901). The contrast between the primitive shoot morphology and the extreme specialization of the inflorescences is indeed striking.

No information seems to be available concerning pollination in *Faurea* and similar genera. The syndrome indicates entomophily. On the other hand, it is reported by seedsmen and breeders that birds are very important pollinators of the loosely organized heads of *Leucospermum*. According to available information the crop of *Leucospermum* seed is directly dependent on the frequency of pollinating birds during the flowering season. However, these brush blossoms are also visited by many other animals, of which the smaller e.g. hive bees, seem to be able to reach the nectar without making contact with the stigmas (observed along the road near Stellenbosch). They must therefore be considered nectar thieves. But a large, green beetle, *Trichostetha fascicularis*, which is known to visit these blossoms (observed in Kirstenbosch gardens), undoubtedly brushes against both stigmas and anthers when it lands on the heads, and probably also pollinates the inflorescences, even if a direct proof has not been given.

Birds are very active feeders in *Protea* blossoms and there is no doubt that they are also important pollinators. According to information, the long-tailed sugarbird, *Promerops cafer,* usually nests in *Protea* bushes and also takes practically all its nourishment from them. The narrow inflorescences of, e.g., *P. repens* (*P. mellifera*) are hardly negotiable by larger insects which would find great difficulty in entering between the massed styles. On the other hand the stiff involucral bracts certainly form very suitable perches for pollinating birds whose beaks reach the bottom of the inflorescence. As to the quantity of nectar available, the synonym as well as its popular name, "sugarbush", are sufficiently indicative. Observations show that *P. repens* is pollinated by birds.

When it comes to the open, bowl-shaped *Protea* blossoms, of which *P. cynaroides* has been quoted as an example, it is evident that they can be utilized by many nectar and pollen collecting animals. They are visited by

Reprinted by permission of the author and the publisher from *The Journal of South African Botany* **31**: 133–136, 1965.

birds, bees, and beetles alike, and as their seed-setting (always irregular) is reported not to show such a close correlation to the occurrence of sugar-birds as in *Leucospermum*, it is not improbable that other groups are, at any rate partly, effective as pollinators.

In *Leucandendron*, the organisation of the blossom indicates that the pollinator should be short-tongued animals. Apparently, the black beetle *Genuchus hottentottus* (observed on Table Mountain) is an effective pollinator of these blossoms. To which extent they are also visited by other insects is unknown: the beetle, on its part, is not restricted to *Leucadendron*, but was also seen in other blossoms of a corresponding organisation (e.g., *Clutia*).

Within *Proteaceae* there is thus a "retrograde" development of pollination syndromes from the brush blossom type back to the more primitive bowl-shaped one concomitant with the progressive morphological development of the blossom. This development is apparently accompanied by a similar "retrograde" development amongst the pollinators, from pure or predominating ornithophily back to the assumed most primitive stage of cantharophily.

* * *

References

Faegri, K. and L. van der Pijl 1966: *Principles of Pollination Ecology.*—Toronto: Pergamon Press.

Johnson, L. A. S. and B. G. Briggs 1963: Evolution in Proteaceae.—*Australian* J. Bot. **11**: 21.

Levyns, M. R. 1964: Presidential address. Migrations and origin of the Cape flora. —*Trans. Roy. Soc. South Africa* **37**: 85.

Marloth, R. 1901: Die Ornithophilie in der Flora Süd-Afrikas.—*Ber. Deutschen Bot. Ges.* **19**: 176.

Vogel, S. 1954: Blütenbiologische Typen als Elemente der Sippengliederung.— *Bot. Stud.* 1.

4 / Ecological Evolution

Different species do not interbreed because they are separated by barriers to hybridization, or *isolating mechanisms*. If the barrier is geographic or ecological the species are *allopatric*. If two species have overlapping ecological ranges, they are *sympatric* and are separated by some type of reproductive or genetic isolation. Allopatric species may or may not be genetically isolated, but sympatric species must be. As populations beome isolated, they find ecological regions or *niches* where they can live and to which they become adapted.

Allopatric and sympatric populations in tree frogs are discussed by Littlejohn; the mating call, a behavioral characteristic, is probably the key isolating mechanism. In gulls, food preference seems to isolate two species; Brown points out that with a great abundance of human refuse the barrier appears to be breaking down. Whether two similar species can occupy the same niche at the same time has been debated. Caplan discusses the subject with relation to food preferences of grasshoppers.

Variation within a population may occur in a series of gradual changes ranging from one extreme to the other. Nelson describes such a *cline* for two forms of each of two races of *Prunella vulgaris* and discusses their habitats.

A large homogeneous population may fragment into several populations occupying different niches to which they become better adapted by natural selection. Steeves describes an example of such *adaptive radiation* in troglobitic asellids; the radiation occurred with the retreat of the seas after the asellids' original invasion of Florida.

Gene mutation, chromosome aberrations, and gene recombination provide the variation on which natural selection acts—the raw materials, in a sense, of evolution; but there is a feedback as the result of which natural selection acts to determine the kind of genetic system that will prevail in a certain ecological situation. Heslop-Harrison, discussing reproductive versatility and the evolution of breeding systems in flowering plants, points out that the environment exerts some control over reproductive systems and that it may sometimes be of adaptive significance.

Premating Isolation in the *Hyla ewingi* Complex (Anura: Hylidae)

M. J. Littlejohn

The geographic ranges of two closely related southeastern Australian anurans, *Hyla ewingi* and *H. verreauxi*, overlap in part so that continuously distributed allopatric and extensive sympatric populations of each species exist, without any hybridization in the latter situation. The existence of a second contact of the two forms north of the Victoria—New South Wales border is suspected but this relatively inaccessible area awaits detailed investigation. In addition, disjunct allopatric populations of *H. ewingi* occur as late Pleistocene isolates on three adjacent continental islands: Tasmania, Flinders Island, and King Island. This distribution pattern appears suitable for a study of geographic variation in actual or potential reproductive isolating mechanisms, since within the species complex it may be possible to assess the applicability of the two main tenets advanced to account for the origin of reproductive isolation (reviewed by Mayr, 1963).

The present problem centers on the development of one type of premating isolating mechanism (Littlejohn, 1957, 1959; Mecham, 1961)—ethological isolation—and whether it arises *incidentally* along with other adaptive processes operating in allopatric populations, or whether through the direct action of selection for the isolating effect itself. Differences in mating call structure may operate as important ethological isolating mechanisms between sympatric species of anurans (Blair, 1955a, 1958; Littlejohn and Michaud, 1959; Littlejohn *et al.*, 1960; Littlejohn, 1960; Michaud, 1962). Since this behavioral characteristic can be objectively analyzed and compared by conventional electronic means it was selected for detailed study. Other possible premating isolating mechanisms such as habitat preferences, calling positions, breeding seasons, and breeding temperatures also were examined.

· · ·

Discussion

Disjunct Allopatric Populations

When the four allopatric populations of *H. ewingi* are compared, a number of statistically significant differences are evident in the mean values of three call components—note duration, pulses per call, and dominant frequency. This call divergence in the allopatric populations may be explained by either or both of two processes: (1) as an incidental by-product of other adaptive processes (Muller, 1940, 1942); or (2) through the influence of different *sound environments* (Littlejohn, 1959; Marler, 1960). Different species of anurans (or other soniferous animals) with similar sound characteristics might be present at the breeding sites of each isolate. Acoustic interference could lead to modification of call structure through the direct action of selection for more efficient communication.

The sound environments of the isolates under consideration are similar, and all the other species of anurans present have mating calls very different from those of *H. ewingi* (Littlejohn, 1959, 1964; Littlejohn and Martin, 1965; Littlejohn, unpublished observations). Accordingly, the differences in call structure seen between the disjunct allopatric populations of *H. ewingi* may best be explained as incidental products of other adaptive processes. A similar explanation was advanced for mating call differentiation in three disjunct allopatric populations of the leptodactylid species, *Crinia signifera* (Littlejohn, 1964).

The allopatric populations of *H. ewingi* were almost certainly continuous with each other during the last glacial period of the Pleistocene when the world sea level was more than 100 meters lower than at present (Godwin *et al.*, 1958; McFarlan, 1961; Fairbridge, 1962). At that time an extensive land bridge connected the three islands together and to the adjacent mainland, across the present water gap, Bass Strait (Littlejohn, 1964; Littlejohn and Martin, 1964). The islands were separated from the Australian mainland about 12,000 years ago, and from each other 11,000 to 9,000 years ago (based on soundings of Bass Strait given by Jennings, 1959, and on the dating of the postglacial recovery of the world sea level by Godwin *et al.*, 1958). Whether the call divergence came about after the separation, or was present during the period of continuous distribution, is not clear. The mean values of note duration and pulses per note follow a latitudinal cline which could have existed before isolation.

As with the isolates of *C. signifera* on Tasmania, Flinders Island, and the adjacent Australian mainland (Littlejohn, 1964), the differences in call structure are not as great as those between congeneric sympatric species, for ranges of variation of each call component overlap. In one component, pulse repetition frequency, the mean values for all isolates are virtually identical. All the synchronously breeding, sympatric species of anurans (which do not form natural hybrids) so far examined have calls which differ markedly in at least one call component, with no overlap, but a distinct gap in ranges of variation (Blair, 1955b, 1956, 1958; Crenshaw and Blair, 1959; Fouquette, 1960; Littlejohn, 1959; Littlejohn and Main, 1959). The degree of differentiation evident in the island populations is not of this order and potential reproductive isolation through the action of this mechanism is unlikely.

Another point of interest is that the calls of the remote allopatric populations of *H. ewingi* (Tasmania) and *H. verreauxi* are remarkably similar, so much so that they cannot be distinguished by the human ear. As with the disjunct allopatric populations of *H. ewingi*, the extensive overlap in ranges of variation of all measured call components would seem to preclude any potential premating isolation between these heterospecific allopatric populations.

Sympatric Populations

The transition from allopatry to sympatry is correlated with pronounced modifications in pulse repetition frequency, pulses per note, and degree of amplitude modulation. These changes are much greater in *H. verreauxi*. The direction of change in values of these three characters is such that differences become accentuated. Amplitude modulation is substantially reduced in calls of many western sympatric individuals of *H. verreauxi*, suggesting a progressive loss of this call characteristic from the western populations. In this area none of the calls of *H. verreauxi* is fully modulated. The two remaining call components, note duration and dominant frequency, do not show this trend but become more similar in one or other of the sympatric areas (*viz.*, note duration in western sympatry and dominant frequency in eastern sympatry). Nevertheless, the call structure of the sympatric populations of the two species is very different with no overlap, but with a clear break in the ranges of variation of pulses per note and pulse repetition frequency. In each of the sympatric areas means of pulses per note and pulse repetition frequency differ by factors of three and two respectively.

Calls of closely related sympatric species of anurans commonly differ in pulse repetition frequency (Blair, 1955b, 1956, 1958; Crenshaw and Blair, 1959; Littlejohn, 1959). In some cases it may be the only really distinctive characteristic in the calls, with the other measured components overlapping to some extent. In call discrimination trials on *Pseudacris triseriata* (Littlejohn, 1960) and *H. versicolor* call races (Littlejohn *et al.*, 1960), female frogs discriminated between two recorded calls in which the pulse repetition values differed by a factor of about two. It seems reasonable to suggest that in these cases it is the pulse repetition frequency which carries the critical information of species identity and on which effective discrimination by females, and the resulting sexual isolation, depend. If this is also true for *H. ewingi* and *H. verreauxi* then the changes in pulse repetition frequency from allopatry into sympatry may be a result of direct selection for increasing efficiency of reproductive isolation between these two species. That is to say, the slight differences already present in the allopatric populations are being reinforced in sympatry in the way suggested by Blair (1955a, 1958) for anuran species pairs in *Microhyla* and *Acris*. Such an explanation would support the hypothesis of the sympatric development of a reproductive isolating mechanism (Fisher, 1930; Sturtevant, 1938; Dobzhansky, 1940; Muller, 1942), and provides another example of one type of character displacement (Brown and Wilson, 1956).

It is conceivable that these changes in call structure reflect interactions with species other than *H. ewingi* and *H. verreauxi*, respectively. However, intensive field work throughout this area, together with an analysis of mating calls of the other anuran species present (unpublished observations), indicate that all these species have quite different call structure. The only other closely related species in southeastern Australia is *Hyla jervisiensis* (Moore, 1961). This species occurs in south coastal New South Wales and eastern Victoria, but is found only rarely in the breeding habitats of *H. ewingi* and *H. verreauxi*. The mating call of *H. jervisiensis* is basically similar to that of *H. ewingi* but differs in having a much longer note duration, more pulses per note, a lower pulse repetition frequency, and a lower dominant frequency (unpublished observations).

One by-product of this suggested process of reinforcing selection is that the ranges of variation of pulse repetition frequency in allopatric and western sympatric *H. verreauxi* do not overlap and are almost as different as those of eastern sympatric *H. ewingi* and *H. verreauxi*. Thus these two remote allopatric populations of the same species may now be potentially reproductively isolated, as are distant populations of *Pseudacris triseriata* (Littlejohn, 1960). If the explanation of call differentiation in the sympatric populations is correct then the changes in the remote populations of *H. verreauxi* have resulted from the influence of different sound environments, i.e., the presence or absence of *H. ewingi*. In this case there is no requirement for the prior development of hybrid incapacitation, an essential condition for reinforcing selection (Mayr, 1963).

The similarity of variances of call components in the allopatric and sympatric populations of each species is surprising. One might have predicted that the call structure of the allopatric populations, free from the selective pressure for specificity, would be more variable; while sympatric populations, under conditions which required distinct call structure, would be less variable (Marler, 1960).

The geographical stability of pulse repetition frequency in the allopatric populations of *H. ewingi*, and the great differences in the sympatric populations of both species support the suggestion that this component is the critical one on which the isolation depends. The lack of variation in pulse repetition frequency values in the allopatric populations of *H. ewingi* may reflect that the basic mechanism of call recognition is deeply entrenched and that only the intense selection pressure for the maintenance of reproductive efficiency in sympatry is sufficient to lead to any marked change in this component.

Summary

1. Two closely related anuran species, *Hyla ewingi* and *H. verreauxi*, have overlapping geographic ranges in coastal southeastern Australia. Geographically isolated populations of *H. ewingi* are also present on at least three adjacent large continental islands.

2. Allopatric and sympatric populations of these two species were examined for indications of geographic variation in mating call structure, a

behavioral character thought to operate as a key premating isolating mechanism.

3. This investigation was directed towards assessing the importance of geographical isolation and sympatry in the development of premating isolation.

4. Calls of the geographically isolated populations of *H. ewingi* (isolated from each other for about 9,000 to 12,000 years) were found to have diverged, but not to a degree which, on the basis of an examination of sympatric species, would allow them to operate as efficient ethological isolating mechanisms. One important component, pulse repetition frequency, showed only slight divergence.

5. Whereas mating calls of remote allopatric populations of *H. ewingi* and *H. verreauxi* are very similar, those of the sympatric populations are quite distinct, differing especially in pulse repetition frequency and extent of amplitude modulation. It is suggested that the marked differences between sympatric populations have resulted from the direct action of selection for increased reproductive efficiency, i.e., the slight differences present in the allopatric populations have been reinforced in the sympatric populations.

6. It is also suggested that pulse repetition frequency, because of its similarity in the alopatric populations, and difference in the sympatric populations (where there is no overlap in ranges of variation), is the critical information bearing component of the mating call on which efficient and specific discrimination depends.

• • •

Literature Cited

Blair, W. F. 1955a. Mating call and stage of speciation in the *Microhyla olivacea-M. carolinensis* complex. *Evolution* **9**: 469–480.

———. 1955b. Differentiation in mating call of spadefoots, genus *Scaphiopus. Texas J. Sci.* **7**: 183–188.

———. 1956. Call difference as an isolation mechanism in southwestern toads (genus *Bufo*). *Texas J. Sci.* **8**: 87–106.

———. 1958. Mating call in the speciation of anuran amphibians. *Amer. Nat.* **92**: 27–51.

Brown, W. L., and E. O. Wilson. 1956. Character displacement. Syst. Zool. **5**: 49–64.

Crenshaw, J. W., and W. F. Blair. 1959. Relationships in the *Pseudacris nigrita* complex in southwestern Georgia. *Copeia* **1959**: 215–222.

Dobzhansky, T. 1940. Speciation as a stage in evolutionary divergence. *Amer. Nat.* **74**: 312–321.

Duméril, A. M. C., and G. Bibron. 1841. *Erpetologie General ou Histoire Naturelle Complete des Reptiles.* Vol. 8. Roret, Paris.

Fairbridge, R. W. 1962. World sea-level and climatic changes. *Quaternaria* **6**: 111–134.

Fisher, R. A. 1930. *The Genetical Theory of Natural Selection.* Clarendon Press, Oxford.

Fouquette, M. J. 1960. Isolating mechanisms in three sympatric treefrogs in the Canal Zone. *Evolution* **14**: 484–497.

Godwin, H., R. P. Suggate, and E. H. Willis. 1958. Radiocarbon dating of the eustatic rise in ocean level. *Nature* **181**: 1518–1519.

Hubbs, C. L., and C. Hubbs. 1953. An improved graphical analysis and comparison of series of samples. *Syst. Zool.* **2**: 49–57.

Jennings, J. N. 1959. The submarine topography of Bass Strait. *Proc. Roy. Soc. Victoria* **71**: 49–72.

Littlejohn, M. J. 1957. The biology of the genus *Crinia*. Ph. D. thesis, Univ. Western Australia, Nedlands.

————. 1959. Call differentiation in a complex of seven species of *Crinia* (Anura: Leptodactylidae). *Evolution* **13**: 452–468.

————. 1960. Call discrimination and potential reproductive isolation in *Pseudacris triseriata* females from Oklahoma. *Copeia* **1960**: 370–371.

————. 1963. Frogs of the Melbourne area. *Victorian Nat.* **79**: 296–304.

————. 1964. Geographic isolation and mating call differentiation in *Crinia signifera*. *Evolution* **18**: 262–266.

————, M. J. Fouquette, and C. Johnson. 1960. Call discrimination by female frogs of the *Hyla vesicolor* complex. *Copeia* **1960**: 47–49.

———— and A. R. Main. 1959. Call structure in two genera of Australian burrowing frogs. *Copeia* **1959**: 266–270.

———— and A. A. Martin. 1964. The *Crinia laevis* complex (Anura: Leptodactylidae) in south-eastern Australia. *Austr. J. Zool.* **12**: 70–83.

————. 1965. Mating call structure in three sympatric species of *Limnodynastes* (Anura: Leptodactylidae). *Copeia*, pp. 509–511.

———— and T. C. Michaud. 1959. Mating call discrimination by females of Strecker's chorus frog (*Pseudacris streckeri*). *Texas J. Sci.* **11**: 86–92.

Marler, P. 1960. Bird songs and mate selection. *In* Animal sounds and communication, Lanyon and Tavolga (ed.). *Amer. Inst. Biol. Sci.*, Washington.

Mayr, E. 1963. *Animal Species and Evolution*. Belknap Press, Harvard.

McFarlan, E. 1961. Radiocarbon dating of late Quaternary deposits, south Louisiana. *Bull. Geol. Soc. Amer.* **72**: 129–158.

Mecham, J. S. 1961. Isolating mechanisms in anuran amphibians. In *Vertebrate Speciation*, Blair (ed.). Univ. Texas Press, Austin.

Michaud, T. C. 1962. Call discrimination by females of the chorus frogs, *Pseudacris clarki* and *Pseudacris nigrita*. *Copeia* **1962**: 213–215.

Moore, J. A. 1961. The frogs of eastern New South Wales. *Bull. Amer. Mus. Nat. Hist.* **121**: 149–386.

Muller, H. J. 1940. Bearings of the "Drosophila" work on systematics. In *The New Systematics*, Huxley (ed.). Oxford University Press, Oxford.

————. 1942. Isolating mechanisms, evolution and temperature. *Biol. Symp.* **6**: 71–125.

Simpson, G. G., A. Roe, and R. C. Lewontin. 1960. *Quantitative Zoology*. Harcourt Brace, New York.

Sturtevant, A. H. 1938. Essays on evolution. III. On the origin of interspecific sterility. *Quart. Rev. Biol.* **13**: 333–335.

Species Isolation between the Herring Gull Larus argentatus and Lesser Black-Backed Gull L. fuscus

R. G. B. Brown

Introduction

The Herring Gull *Larus argentatus* and the Lesser Black-backed Gull *L. fuscus* are the classic example of a "ring" species (Mayr 1963). They are the two ends of a ring of subspecies which have come to overlap. Despite their close relationship, and the fact that they can produce fertile hybrids (e.g., Tinbergen 1953), there is practically complete species isolation between the two in their region of overlap in northwest Europe.

During the summers of 1962–65 I worked in the large, mixed gullery on Walney Island, in northwest Lancashire, England. There are about 9000 pairs of each species in this colony, nesting side by side and at the very high average density of one nest per 40 square yards. But during these four seasons I never saw a mixed pair, and I saw only one bird which appeared to be a hybrid. The isolation mechanism is obviously very efficient.

This situation raises two questions for the field worker. First, what is the species isolation mechanism, and secondly, why should it be important for these two closely related birds to stay apart, instead of interbreeding? I have tried to answer these questions from my work on Walney. The answers are not conclusive, though I think they help to clarify the possibilities.

• • •

Summary

There is a large, mixed colony of the two "ring" species, the Herring Gull *Larus argentatus* and Lesser Black-backed Gull *L. fuscus*, on Walney Island, northwest Lancashire. These birds are nesting at the very high density of one nest/40 square yards, or more, but although they defend their territories against both species indiscriminately, there is effectively no hybridization. This paper discusses the nature of the species isolation mechanism, and its function.

Since the two species can produce fertile hybrids, the mechanism must be of an ecological/behavioural nature, rather than morphological incompatibility. It is shown that there are slight differences in breeding season and

Reprinted by permission of the author and the British Ornithologists' Union from *The Ibis* **109**: 310–317, 1967.

habitat, but these do not seem to be great enough to account for the high degree of isolation.

It is likely that species isolation depends primarily on the female's choice of a mate. It is suggested that, as specific cues, she uses the differences in call-note tones, and the colour of the back (and perhaps also of the eye-ring), or both.

Herring Gulls and Lesser Black-backs are adapted to slightly different niches. The overlap is so great, however, that any hybrid is unlikely to be at a disadvantage; but the overlap can only have arisen very recently, as a result of both species taking advantage of the increased availability of human refuse. It is possible that the isolation mechanism was evolved to cope with earlier conditions, when food was more limited, and the species' niches more sharply defined.

References

Barnes, J. A. G. 1961. The winter status of the Lesser Black-backed Gull 1959–60. *Bird Study* **8**: 127–147.

Beer, C. G. 1963. Incubation and nest-building behaviour of Black-headed Gulls. IV. Nestbuilding in the laying and incubation periods. *Behaviour* **21**: 155–176.

Fisher, J. and R. M. Lockley. 1954. *Sea Birds*. London: Collins.

Goethe, F. 1963. Verhaltensunterschiede zwischen europaischen Formen der Silbermowengrupper (*Larus argentatus—cacchinans—fuscus*). *J. Orn.* **104**: 129–141.

Harris, M. P. 1964a. Aspects of the breeding biology of the gulls *Larus argentatus*, *L. fuscus* and *L. marinus*. *Ibis* **106**: 432–456.

——. 1964b. Recoveries of ringed Herring Gulls. *Bird Study* **11**: 183–191.

——. 1965. The food of some *Larus* gulls. *Ibis* **107**: 43–53.

Mayr, E. 1963. *Animal Species and Evolution*. Cambridge, Mass. : Harvard U.P.

Paludan, K. 1951. Contributions to the breeding biology of *Larus argentatus* and *Larus fuscus*. *Vidensk. Medd dansk naturh. Foren.* **114**: 1–128.

Tinbergen, N. 1953. *The Herring Gull's World*. London: Collins.

——. 1959. Comparative studies of the behaviour of gulls (Laridae): a progress report. *Behaviour* **15**: 1–70.

Differential Feeding and Niche Relationships among Orthoptera

Elizabeth Bruning Caplan

Abstract

The acridian species *Melanoplus bivittatus* (Say), *Melanoplus differentialis* (Thomas) and *Melanoplus lakinus* (Scudder) occur in the same habitat, utilizing the same foods. Such coexistence suggests that these species are in the same niche and in competition for a common food supply. Their food usages were investigated by offering samples of dominant and semi-dominant vegetation from the common habitat to caged populations of each species, then estimating the amount consumed. The over-all usage of foods of each species formed a preferential pattern sufficiently different from the patterns of the other two species to indicate that the three grasshopper populations occupy separate niches in the community and are not in complete competition for food.

Introduction

Gause's Principle holds that two or more similar species cannot coexist indefinitely in the same niche without diverging in their ecological requirements. If ecological divergence does not take place, the species with a slight advantage in competition for any limited factor of the environment will eventually displace others.

Although the niche of a species includes more than its use of foods, food choice is a significant criterion upon which to base niche relationships. Biologists have noted that closely related species of grasshoppers feed upon the same grasses and forbs in given habitats, thus appearing to co-occupy a food niche. Such co-occupancy would be a refutation of Gause's Principle. However, Isely (1946), Gangwere (1961) and others have pointed out that apparent non-differentiation in food selection may be superficial; their studies indicate that grasshopper species feeding together exhibit distinct and separate food preferences.

In this paper the coexistence of *Melanoplus bivittatus* (Say), *M. differentialis* (Thomas) and *M. lakinus* (Scudder) is considered. These congeneric species of the family Acrididae are found feeding together in the grassland habitats of the Boulder, Colorado region. While one species, *M. lakinus*, is distinct in size and other features, the other two are closely related in all characters. Do these species occupy one niche in the habitat where they are found, or are they segregated into separate niches by their preference for different foods?

• • •

Reprinted by permission of the author and publisher from *Ecology* **47**: 1074–1076, 1966.

Results and Discussion

Table 1 summarizes the data collected July through September. A visual estimate was made of the percentage of each plant consumed by the grasshoppers.

Melanoplus bivittatus, M. differentialis and *M. lakinus* are described, generally, as indiscriminate forb and grass eaters, selecting food from a wide variety of plant species. However, different patterns in their use of foods are demonstrated by the data of Table 1.

The two larger grasshoppers did not differ significantly in their use of *Conium maculatum* (poison hemlock), *Tragopogon dubius, Taraxacum officinale, Avena sativa, Medicago sativa* and *Plantago lanceolata*. The differences in the amounts eaten of these plant species were within 20%, a divergence thought insignificant under the visual method of estimation. However, there was a large divergence in utilization of dominant plants from the two habitats. *M. bivittatus* ate 5% of *Agrostis gigantea*, whereas *M. differentialis* ate 80% of the same plant. *M. bivittatus* ate 5% of *Trifolium pratense* and

TABLE 1

Plants fed to grasshoppers and estimates of percentages eaten

Plant species	Percent Eaten		
	M. bivittatus	M. differentialis	M. lakinus
Conium maculatum	90	100	10
Tragopogon dubius	80	90	10
Taraxacum officinale	90	80	25
Avena sativa	60	50	60
Medicago sativa	40	40–50	20
Plantago lanceolata	60	40	40
Agrostis gigantea	5	80	50
Trifolium pratense	5	60	10–15
Dactylis glomerata	80	50	80
Carum carvi	75	0	20
Argemone intermedia	85	15	10
Melotius alba	70	40	60
Ambrosia psilostachya	10	40	10
Marrubium vulgare	5	25	5
Verbascum thapsis	15	0	5
Saponaria officinalis	10	10	15
Rosa arkansana	10	15	15
Agropyron cristatum	5	20	5
Agropyron repens	5	30	20
Ambrosia trifida	10	30	25
Convolvulus arvensis	10	15	20
Kochia scoparia	5	30	10
Mentha spicata	30	50	20
Sporobolus cryptandrus	10	30	30

M. differentialis ate 60%. Less divergence but a notable variation of selection for the dominant species *Dactylis glomerata* occurred. There was also a large divergence in selection for the semi-dominant vegetation of these fields. *M. bivittatus* ate 75% of *Carum carvi* and *M. differentialis* ate none, although the plant remained in the feeding cage for the three day period. *M. bivittatus* ate 85% of *Argemone intermedia* but *M. differentialis* ate only 15%. Less divergence was noted in the selection of *Melotius alba, Ambrosia psilostachya* and *Marrubium vulgare.*

The small grasshopper, *Melanoplus lakinus*, exhibited a different feeding pattern from that of *M. bivittatus* and *M. differentialis*. Such plants as *Conium maculautm*, eaten 100% by *M. differentialis* and 90% by *M. bivittatus* were only 10% consumed by *M. lakinus*. Other obvious differences were the amounts of *Tragopogon dubius* and *Taraxacum officinale* eaten by the three species of grasshoppers. There was a correspondence of utilization among *M. bivittatus, M. differentialis* and *M. lakinus* for the abundant oats supply and for *Dactylis glomerata.*

There is no noticeable restriction to one or a few plants by any of the grasshoppers studied. None of the *Melanoplus* species of this study exhibits a complete restriction to grasses or to forbs, nor do the data indicate that either grasses or forbs are more extensively utilized. Such patterns did not arise from further data collected in 1964 based on plant species offered to the grasshoppers from other habitats. Among the three grasshopper species there is, however, a common failure to feed extensively on such species as *Verbascum thapsis, Saponaria officinalis* and *Rosa arkansana.*

The food usages of *Melanoplus bivittatus, M. differentialis* and *M. lakinus* are sufficiently different to indicate that the three species occupy separate niches. The data from this experiment, however, apply to only one factor of the niche, that of food preference. Albeit food preference is an obvious criterion to use in the separation of animal relationships, it is only one of several factors, and further studies might be made among these generalized feeders as to their other niche requirements.

It was noted that the relative numbers of individuals of these three species varied significantly throughout the summer; such varying population densities in each season may lessen competition between them. September collections show a decrease in the number of *Melanoplus bivittatus*, which was the most common grasshopper in August, and an almost complete disappearance of *M. lakinus*. In September, there was a great rise in the number of *M. differentialis* individuals. Position in the habitat also varied. In Long's field where oats were cultivated, *M. bivittatus* was found throughout the area, whereas its potential competitor, *M. differentialis*, was more often found near the eastern border by roadside weeds and grasses such as *Ambrosia psilostachya* and *Agrostis gigantea*. The distribution reflects usage of the latter foods by *M. differentialis* but also might reflect displacement from the center of the field by populations of *M. bivittatus*.

As a final note on numbers and position, it was observed that the grass-hopper distribution altered when the oats were harvested in the latter half of August. The stalks were collected in the south side of the field as a hay-stack; *M. bivittatus* swarmed upon the haystack but *M. differentialis* was uncommon there. *M. differentialis* was found in ridges of rubble left in the field. However, by September 4, it was difficult to collect *M. bivittatus* on or in the haystack, yet *M. differentialis* was common there. By this date *M. lakinus* had apparently disappeared from the area.

In conclusion, the most obvious pattern to arise from the data was the separation of the food usage of *Melanoplus lakinus* from that of *M. bivittatus* and *M. differentialis*. However, divergences in usage between *M. bivittatus* and *M. differentialis* were also striking, in particular in the utilization of *Carum carvi*, *Agrostis gigantea*, *Argemone intermedia*, *Trifolium pratense*, *Melotius alba* and *Ambrosia psilostachya*. From these data, I have concluded that the food usages are sufficiently distinct and divergent among these three species to suggest the separation of these grasshoppers into different niches in the community.

$$\bullet \quad \bullet \quad \bullet$$

Literature Cited

Gangwere, S. K. 1961. A monograph on food selection in Orthoptera. *Trans. Amer. Entomol. Soc.* **87**: 67–230.

Isley, F. B. 1946. Differential feeding in relation to local distribution of grasshoppers. *Ecology* **27**: 128–138.

Racial Diversity in Californian *Prunella vulgaris*

Andrew P. Nelson

Summary

Two sequential common garden studies of Californian *Prunella vulgaris* subsp. *lanceolata* have revealed the existence of a first-year flowering low-elevation race adapted to mild winters and a second-year flowering montane race adapted to severe winters. Characteristics of habit and growth rate provide for the recognition of coastal and inland forms within the low-elevation race and Cascade and Sierran forms within the montane race. The distribution of these four racial forms in California can be correlated with climatological features. Clinal variation correlated with latitude and elevation can be demonstrated within each form. A sequence by which the four forms might have evolved is postulated. Comparison of the results obtained with published accounts of variation in European *P. vulgaris* and other Californian species suggests that modes of infraspecific variation in California and Europe may be more comparable than previous studies would indicate.

• • •

Discussion

The Pattern of Population Variation

Californian populations of *Prunella vulgaris* subsp. *lanceolata* may be divided into two major groups. The first, comprising a low-elevation race, includes plants which, in cultivation, are often capable of flowering heavily during the first season of growth and rarely capable of surviving severe winter conditions. These populations occur at the immediate sea coast and inland at low-elevation sites in the valleys of major streams and rivers. The second group comprises a montane race. It consists of populations in which the constituent plants flower only during the second season in cultivation and in which a reasonably high proportion of the plants are capable of surviving a rigorous winter at the end of their first season of growth.

Each of these two races may be subdivided into two forms. Plants of coastal populations of the low-elevation race represented in this study were shorter and broader relative to their height than plants from inland populations. Coastal plants had slightly broader cauline leaves than inland representatives of the low-elevation race and tended to flower slightly earlier than inland plants from comparable latitudes. The strongly ascending to nearly erect floral shoots of inland plants developed from a caespitose rosette of long, narrow, centrally attached basal leaves. The floral shoots of coastal

Reprinted by permission of the author and Trustees of the *New Phytologist* **66**: 707–746, 1967.

plants arose from more actively growing basal shoots which collectively took the form of a pulvinate rosette or even a repent mat. The coastal form of the low-elevation race occupies an apparently continuous physiographic region while the distribution of the inland form is highly discontinuous.

During their first season, plants from the Cascade samples developed a pulvinate rosette of densely packed irregularly arranged leaves which, in the second season, gave rise to a decumbent plant, spreading at the base but with ultimately ascending floral shoots. In Sierran samples, development was initiated by the formation of a caespitose rosette of centrally attached leaves followed in the second season by the formation of a basally more centralized plant with moderately ascending floral shoots. The Sierran sequence may be extrapolated south to include the San Bernardino population. The similarity between Cascade and high-elevation Coast Range samples and between Sierran and mid-elevation Coast Range samples can be reconciled by postulating an extension of the range of the Cascade form into the Coast Ranges and the existence of two geographically separated ranges for the Sierran form.

There is abundant evidence of clinal variation within the four racial forms. In both forms of the low-elevation race it is often possible to correlate the position of a given sample on a character gradient with the latitude of the site from which it was collected. The nature of the Lake Shasta sample suggests that extremes of elevation may modify such correlations. Within the montane materials it appears that an interrelationship between latitude and elevation may serve to control the position of population sample on a particular character gradient.

The geographic boundary between the low-elevation race and the montane race is marked by populations which mix the characteristic flowering and overwintering potentials of the two races in varying degrees and combinations. Recognition, in samples from such populations, of structure and habit characteristic of the coastal form of the low-elevation race suggests that these mixed populations may be the result of direct contact between the coastal form and the Sierran form of the montane race. Field observations suggest that contact between these two forms is discontinuous and that there is significant geographic separation between coastal and Sierran forms along much of the boundary which separates them.

The combination of inland low-elevation habit and montane over-wintering potential characterized samples from the Eel River Valley and a suggestion of typical inland low-elevation habit was recognized in the weak first-year flowering plants of sample 606 from the valley of the Smith River. Both of these areas might, on a geographic basis, be expected to harbour populations of the inland form of the low-elevation race. Although the Eel River sequence, included in the Hanover experiment, does not extend completely across the boundary between the low-elevation and montane races, it does suggest that gradients in characteristics such as date of flowering may traverse this boundary locally. There are only three population samples (579, 660 and 680) which were so consistently unique when considered in the context of their geographic origin that they cannot be designated as members of or intermediates between any of the four racial forms described above. It is possible that populations recorded from Baja California (e.g. C. H. Low, Jr 3060—R. M. Turner 59—166 and K. L. Chambers, 924, DS) might provide some understanding of the Mount Palomar population. Further study is required to determine whether the Fish Camp and Hat Creek populations are typical representatives of local materials in their respective areas, before explanations can be advanced for their failure to express characteristics of the racial forms within the range of which they occur.

Basis of Racial Distribution

The coastal form of the low-elevation race of Californian *Prunella vulgaris* subsp. *lanceolata* is restricted to a region falling within the Csn (coastal fog belt) climate as designated by the application of Köppen's system of climatic classification to California (Russell, 1926). This region is marked by moderate temperatures with a minimum of seasonal variation. Sprague (1941) gives average growing seasons, as determined by the period between killing frosts, of from 271 to 328 days for four stations within the latitudinal and elevational range of the coastal form. He notes that 'freezing weather is infrequent on the immediate coast to the northern boundary of the state.' The distribution of the montane race extends from mesothermal Cs'ab and Csb climatic regions to microthermal Ds regions (Russell, 1926). For the most part, these are regions of continental climate with marked seasonal temperature differences. With the possible exception of areas in the Coast Ranges where it may extend to lower elevations, the montane race occupies a region typified by winter frosts and snow accumulation.

Data from five Cascade and eight Sierran weather stations selected for their proximity and latitudinal and elevational correspondence to known populations of *P. vulgaris* show that frosts may occur at any time during the year within the Cascade distribution of the species while sites within the Sierran region experience a minimum frost-free season of over 2 months during the summer (U.S. Weather Bureau 1948–60). Three of these Cascade stations are included in Sprague's tabulations and have average growing seasons of from 72 to 82 days, while the six Sierran stations included have average growing seasons of from 114 to 172 days (Sprague, 1941). Whether or not these data have meaning for the ground-level sites occupied by populations of *P. vulgaris*, it is evident that the Cascade form must be able to withstand lower temperature extremes during the growing season than the Sierran form as it exists on the west slope of the Sierra Nevada. Experimental materials from montane populations in the North Coast Ranges were not sufficiently abundant to serve as a basis for specific designation of the position of the western boundary between Cascade and Sierran forms. Thus, it is not possible to select appropriate data for the investigation of climatological differences between the areas occupied by the two forms in that region. However, the fact that Coast Range populations of the Cascade form were found at a higher elevation than that occupied by the Sierran form suggests that a climatological relationship involving extremes of low temperature during the growing season may separate the ranges of the two forms here as well as in the Cascades and the Sierra Nevada. The San Bernardino and Mount Palomar sites are climatologically related to the Sierran region having minimum frost-free seasons of approximately 4 months (U. S. Weather Bureau 1948–60).

Postulation of correlations between available climatological data and the distribution of the inland form of the low-elevation race is precluded by the limited, discontinuous occurrence of this form and the lack of coincidence between sites occupied by its populations and stations supplying climatological data. Personal observation suggests that the areas occupied by this form experience greater seasonal fluctuations in temperature than coastal sites, but probably have much milder winters than most sites within the range of the montane race.

The distribution of the two montane forms of Californian *P. vulgaris* is strongly suggestive of invasion from the north along the principal north-south mountain systems. The postulation that Sierran and mid-elevation Coast Range populations belong to the same race is consistent with this suggestion, if it can be assumed that a primary invasion was achieved by the Sierran form, that this form branched into the North Coast Ranges and the Cascade–Sierran system and that, following climatic change, it was replaced in the Cascades and the higher elevations of the Coast Ranges by the Cascade form. Disjunct populations south of the Sierra Nevada in the San Bernardino Mountains, the San Jacinto Mountains, and on Mount Palomar suggest a past extension of montane forms south of their present range. The location and exceptional nature of the Mount Palomar population suggest that it might be a relic of a third montane form antedating both the Sierran and the Cascade forms in California. Such a history is consistent with suggestion of repeated north-south advances and retreats of temperate montane elements in the Californian flora during the Pleistocene (Munz, 1959, pp. 9–10).

The apparently continuous distribution of the coastal form of the low-elevation race and the discontinuous nature of its contact with the montane race suggest the possibility of a historical identity for this form as well as for the two montane forms. Present distribution gives no basis for choosing between a number of alternative explanations for the existence of a coastal form in California. Apparent continuity to the north suggests the possibility of invasion and southward migration by an already differentiated coastal form with northern orgins. The possibility that the Sierran form once enjoyed a more widespread distribution in southern montane portions of the state implies that it may also have achieved a more general distribution at low elevations adjacent to the coast. Under such conditions, generalized or repeated local differentiation of the coastal form from the Sierran form might have occurred. Whether its differentiation represented a unique event or a repeated occurrence, a general and widespread or a local phenomenon, the apparent genetic and distributional continuity of coastal populations may be interpreted as the result of origin from a common, although possibly variable, ancestral source and subsequent migration and evolution. Thus they comprise a racial form in a genetic and evolutionary as well as a descriptive and ecological sense.

The discontinuous distribution of the inland form of the low-elevation race might result from the restriction of a once more widespread form or from the local differentiation of coastal or montane forms in appropriate habitats. However, plants of these inland populations express an integrated combination of coastal and Sierran characteristics. Except for the Shasta Lake population, inland low-elevation populations occupy sites along the boundary between the coastal and Sierran forms. Thus these populations may well represent the local stabilization and persistence in appropriate habitats of types derived through hybridization between the coastal and Sierran forms. It is even possible that the Shasta Lake population represents the results of hybridization between coastal populations at the shores of prehistoric inland waters in the Sacramento Valley and Sierran populations which may have occupied the region prior to invasion by the Cascade form. These inland populations are classified as a distinct racial form on the supposition that the similarity of cultivated samples implies a similarity in the circumstances surrounding their possibly independent origins and differentiation.

The samples from the Eel River Valley form a group to which a degree of uniformity in expression of characteristics gives identity and within which it is possible to identify elements of clinal variation which presumably indicate adaptive adjustment to local gradients of environmental variation. Thus these populations express, on a local scale, a coherence and pattern of variation comparable to that expressed on a regional scale by the forms of the low-elevation and montane races. However, the Eel River samples are not related to other intermediate samples by a unique character combination such as that which relates populations of each of the four racial forms. Differentiation of local population groups at points of current or past contact between the coastal and Sierran forms would appear to be a direct function of the selective action of local environments on the range of available biotypes. Subjection of populations in different areas of inter-racial contact to similar selective pressure might produce geographically discontinuous groups of comparable populations such as the inland form of the low-elevation race. In the case of other contact areas, lack of environmental correspondence would lead to isolated local population groups similar only to the extent that they combine in various combinations the characteristics of their common ancestral types. Such population groups are perhaps best designated as racially undifferentiated intermediates between geographically adjacent racial forms.

• • •

References

Baker, H. G. (1953). Race formation and reproductive methods in flowering plants. *Symp. Soc. exp. Biol.* **7**, 114.

Biel, E. R. (1961). Microclimate, bioclimatology and notes on comparative dynamic climatology. *Am. Scient.* **49**, 326.

Björkman, O. and P. Holmgren. (1963). Adaptability of the photosynthetic apparatus to light intensity in ecotypes from exposed and shaded habitats. *Physiologia Pl.* **16**, 889.

Böcher, T. W. (1940). Introductory studies on variation and life-forms in *Prunella vulgaris* L. *Dansk. bot. Ark.* **10** (3), 1.

————. (1945). Some experiments to elucidate the influence of winter conditions on shoot development and floral initiation on various races of *Prunella vulgaris* and *Ranunculus acer. Dansk Bot. Ark.* **12** (3), 1.

————. (1949). Racial divergences in *Prunella vulgaris* in relation to habitat and climate. *New Phytol.* **48**, 285.

————. (1963). The study of ecotypical variation in relation to experimental morphology. *Regnum Veg.* **27**, 10.

————, K. Larsen. and K. Rahn. (1955). Experimental and cytological studies on plant species. III. *Plantago coronopus* and allied species. *Hereditas.* **41**, 423.

Bradshaw, A. D. (1959). Popuation differentiation in *Agrostis tenuis* Sibth. I. Morphological differentiation. *New Phytol.* **58**, 208.

Clausen, J. (1960). A simple method for the sampling of natural populations. *Rep. Scott. Pl. Breed. Stn* 1960, 69.

————, D. Keck. and W. M. Hiesey. (1940). Experimental studies on the nature of species. I. Effect of varied environments on western North American plants. *Publs Carnegie Instn* **520**.

————. (1948). Experimental studies on the nature of species. III. Environmental responses of climatic races of *Achillea. Publs Carnegie Instn* **581**.

Domin, K. (1938). *Prunella vulgaris* L. and *Orchis maculata* L., a study on the variability of two species of the Czechoslovak flora. *Bull. int., Ceska Akad. ved a Umeni.* **39**, 130.

Fernald, M. L. (1913). The indigenous varieties of *Prunella vulgaris* in North America. *Rhodora* **15**, 179.

————. (1950). *Gray's Manual of Botany.* 8th edn. American Book Co., New York.

Fryxell, P. A. (1957). Mode of reproduction of higher plants. *Bot. Rev.* **23**, 135.

Geiger, R. (1950). *The Climate Near the Ground.* Harvard University Press, Cambridge.

Goodwin, R. H. (1944). The inheritance of flowering time in a short-day species, *Solidago sempervirens* L. *Genetics* **29**, 503.

Gregor, J. W. (1956). Adaptation and ecotypic components. *Proc. R. Soc.* B **145**, 333.

————, V. McM. Davey. and J. M. S. Lang. (1936). Experimental taxonomy. I. Experimental garden technique in relation to the recognition of small taxonomic units. *New Phytol.* **35**, 323.

————. and Watson, P. J. (1961). Ecotypic differentiation: observations and reflections. *Evolution* **15**, 166.

Hall, H. M. (1924–28). Entries 719 and 897 in a notebook in the possession of the Department of Plant Biology, Carnegie Institution of Washington, Stanford, California.

Hara, H. (1948). *Enumeratio Spermatophytarum Japonicarum.* Iwanami Shoten, Tokyo.

Harberd, D. J. (1958). Progress and prospects in genecology. *Rep. Scott. Pl. Breed. Stn* 1958, 52.

————. (1961). The case for extensive rather than intensive sampling in genecology. *New Phytol.* **60**, 325.

Heslop-Harrison, J. (1964). Forty years of genecology. *Adv. ecol. Res.* **2**, 159.

Heywood, V. H. (1959). The taxonomic treatment of ecotypic variation. *Publs Systematics Ass.* **3**, 87.

Hultén, E. (1949). *Flora of Alaska and Yukon*, vol. 9. C. W. K. Gleerup, Lund.

Munz, P. A. (1959). *A California Flora.* University of California Press, Berkeley.

Nakai, T. (1930). Notulae ad plantas Japoniae & Koreae. XXXVIII. *Bot. Mag., Tokyo*, **44**, 19.

Nelson, A. P. (1962). *A genecological study in* Prunella vulgaris. *L. (Labiatae)*. Ph. D. thesis, University of California, Berkeley.

————. (1964). Relationships between two subspecies in a population of *Prunella vulgaris* L. *Evolution* **18**, 43.

————. (1965). Taxonomic and evolutionary implications of lawn races in *Prunella vulgaris* (Labiatae). *Brittonia* **17**, 160.

Rubtzoff, P. (1953). A phytogeographical analysis of the Pitkin Marsh. *Wasmann J. Biol.* **2**, 129.

Russell, R. J. (1926). Climates of California. *Univ. Calif. Publs, Geogr.* **2**(4), 73.

Salisbury, E. (1961). *Weeds and Aliens.* Collins, London.

Snedecor, G. W. (1956). *Statistical Methods*, 5th edn. Iowa State College Press, Ames.

Sprague, M. (1941). Climate of California. *Yb. Agric. U.S. Dep. Agric.* 1941, 783.

Turesson, G. (1922). The genotypical response of the plant species to the habitat. *Hereditas* **3**, 211.

U.S. Weather Bureau (1948–60). California. In *Climatological Data for the United States by Sections*, vols. 35–47.

Evolutionary Aspects of the Troglobitic Asellids of the United States: The Hobbsi, Stygius and Cannulus Groups

Harrison R. Steeves, III

Abstract

The affinities and distribution of three groups of troglobitic asellids of the United States are presented. The origin of these three groups of asellids is considered to be monophyletic, from a single invasion of the subterranean water system in Florida, followed by adaptive radiation in the complex of limestone caves formed during the Pliocene and Pleistocene.

A redescription of *Asellus antricolus* is presented with pertinent data concerning variations, new localities, and range of the species. A new species, *A. nortoni*, is described and figured.

Introduction

In establishing an evolutionary scheme for the troglobitic asellids of the United States the investigator is immediately confronted with a number of problems, the most pressing of which are the lack of a fossil record, confusion concerning the taxonomy of these organisms, and insufficient collecting.

The first of these problems, the lack of a fossil record, has no present solution, and the investigator must turn to some other means of formulating opinions as to a possible evolutionary sequence. The most natural step would appear to be a study of the anatomy of these organisms and an attempt to establish, through a comparative study of certain structures, a "hypothetical ancestor" from which to lay the groundwork for an evolutionary hypothesis. Since the fields of taxonomy and evolution are so closely related, it would appear that structures utilized in taxonomy would also be valuable in a study of the evolution of the troglobitic asellids, and such is indeed the case. It should be emphasized, however, that a great deal of confusion has existed concerning the use of certain taxonomic criteria, and it has been only recently that the anatomy of the most significant taxon has been satisfactorily interpreted.

A number of characteristics are useful in classification of the troglobitic asellids, but certain of these have only a limited value, if any, in the establishment of an evolutionary pattern. The male gnathopod has proved quite useful for taxonomic purposes, but only where a collection has a sufficient number of specimens to compare these appendages for possible abnormal conditions

Reprinted by permission of the author and publisher from *The American Midland Naturalist*
75: 392–403, 1966.

due to breakage and regeneration. The uropods are likewise subject to breakage and regeneration, and a careful examination of a number of specimens is needed before any taxonomic value is placed on this particular structure. Both the gnathopod and uropod of the male are also subject to changes with age of the organism, those of older (larger) individuals exhibiting a greater differentiation than those of younger forms. The male second pleopod has proved to be valuable in certain cases where it exhibits unusual structure. Among all the structures utilized for classification, the single most important one is the endopodial tip of the male second pleopod. This structure remains quite constant from one locality to the next for a single species, and is not affected by breakage and regeneration or by the age of the organism. These characteristics are necessary for the establishment of a definite taxonomic key, and subsequently for any study of evolution within this group of organisms. In discussing the evolution of the troglobitic asellids, therefore, only a single taxonomic characteristic will be considered, the armament of the endopodial tip of the male second pleopod, which has proved to be the most consistent anatomical feature.

Insufficient collecting has further complicated any study of evolutionary aspects of the troglobitic asellids by prohibiting the accurate determination of geographical distributions. This condition has been somewhat alleviated in the past few years with an increase in the interest of various investigators for the collection of cave faunas. There are, however, certain species which have been described from either a single locality, or at best from only a few closely associated areas. Any attempt to determine geographical distributions in these instances would be highly speculative to say the least. For this reason, only the geographical distribution of the group as a whole will be considered in this discussion.

•   •   •

Origin of the Troglobitic Asellids

The origin of the troglobitic asellids of the Hobbsi, Stygius, and Cannulus groups appears to have been through a single invasion of the subterranean water systems in Florida. This hypothesis is presented largely because no study of the anatomy of the endopodial tip of the epigean forms has been conducted and it is the only recourse now available. It should be emphasized that in order for the present evolutionary scheme to be acceptable, a thorough study of the epigean forms must be conducted.

There is, however, a certain amount of evidence in support of the assumed monophyletic origin of these three groups. In the first place, the most generalized forms, the members of the Hobbsi group, are found in the underground water systems of Florida, while the most specialized forms, the members of the Cannulus group, occupy the extreme northern portion of the range for these groups (the northwestern portion of West Virginia). Furthermore, the most primitive member of the Hobbsi group (*A. parvus*) occupies an area in central Florida which was apparently an insular land mass during the highest Pleistocene level of the sea (Cooke, 1945), enabling the survival of either *A. parvus* or the pro-*parvus* stock which gave rise to it. As has been previously postulated (Hobbs, 1958), the development of subterranean water systems in the Eocene limestone of the eastern portion of Florida, and the deflection of surface waters into these systems, were conducive to the invasion of these hypogean waters by epigean forms. Such seems to have been the case with the asellids of this region, the result being the successful invasion of these underwater systems by the pro-*parvus* stock. Once this stock had become established in Florida (probably during the Pleistocene), it would appear that adaptive radiation occurred with the subsequent retreat of the seas. As the previously submerged areas became exposed, this radiation occurred in a northerly direction through the subterranean systems of those states where the groups are presently located.

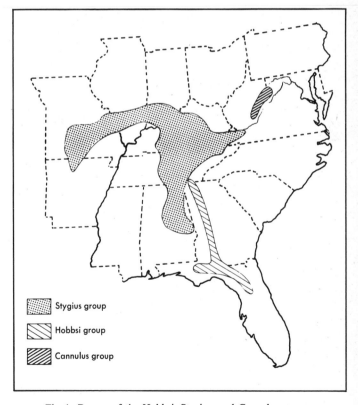

Fig. 1. Ranges of the Hobbsi, Stygius, and Cannulus groups.

References

Cooke, C. W. 1945. Geology of Florida. *Florida Geol. Sur., Geol. Bull.* **29**: 1–399.

Creaser, E. P. 1931. A new blind isopod of the genus *Caecidotea* from a Missouri Cave. *Occ. Pap. Mus. Zool., Univ. Michigan* No. 222: 1–7.

Hay, W. P. 1902. Observations on the crustacea fauna of Nickajack Cave, Tennessee, and vicinity. *Proc. U. S. Nat. Mus.* **25**: 417–439.

Hobbs, H. H., Jr. 1958. The evolutionary history of the pictus Group of the crayfish Genus *Procambarus* (Decapoda, Astacidae). *Quart. J. Florida Acad. Sci.* **21**: 71–91.

Levi, H. W. 1949. Two new species of cave isopods from Pennsylvania. *Notulae Naturae (Acad. Nat. Sci. Philadelphia)* No. 220: 1–6.

Mackin, J. G. 1959. [Isopods], p. 872–878. *In* W. T. Edmonson (ed.) *Ward and Whipple's Freshwater Biology.*

———— and L. Hubricht. 1940. Descriptions of seven new species of *Caecidotea*. *Trans. Amer. Microscop. Soc.* **59**: 383–397.

Miller, M. A. 1933. A new blind isopod, *Asellus californicus*, and a revision of the subterranean asellids. *Univ. California Pub. Zool.* **39**: 97–110.

Steeves, H. R., III. 1960. A contribution toward a knowledge of troglobitic species of the genus Asellus in North America. Master's thesis, University of Virginia, Charlottesville.

———— 1963. The troglobitic asellids of the United States: The Stygius Group. *Amer. Midl. Natur.* **69**: 470–481.

———— 1964. The troglobitic asellids of the United States: The Hobbsi Group. *Ibid.* **71**: 445–451.

———— 1965. Two new species of troglobitic asellids from the United States. *Ibid.* **73**: 81–84.

Van Name, W. G. 1936. The American land and fresh-water isopod Crustacea. *Bull. Amer. Mus. Natur. Hist.* **71**: 474–476.

Reflections on the Role of Environmentally-Governed Reproductive Versatility in the Adaptation of Plant Populations

J. Heslop-Harrison

Although the role of the genetic system in the adaptive evolution of flowering-plant populations received less than due attention in early genecological studies, the neglect has been adequately compensated for in more recent years (Baker, 1953, 1959; Stebbins, 1950, 1957, 1958; Grant, 1958), and it does not seem over-optimistic to suppose that we now have a tolerably comprehensive picture of the ways in which evolutionary response —and in consequence variation pattern—tends to be related to chromosomal properties and breeding behaviour. From the theoretical basis provided by Darlington (1939) and Mather (1943) we can see, furthermore, how breeding systems and reproductive mechanisms are themselves subject to evolutionary change, with the feed-back network provided by natural selection acting, so to speak, in a retrospective mode to determine what kinds of genetic system will prevail in different ecological situations. The consequence of evolution in the genetic systems of flowering plants has indeed been spectacular, for in respect to diversity in reproductive method and breeding-system control the group is quite unrivalled. Angiosperms provide examples of all types of sex expression and incompatibility device—including some, like dichogamy, peculiarly their own—and they reveal an unparalleled virtuosity in the exploitation of chromosome mechanics to achieve various genetical consequences, from unfettered recombination to apomixis. It is also characteristic of flowering plants that they frequently exhibit different types of behaviour simultaneously, expressing what Darlington (1939) has called reproductive versatility.

The best known examples of reproductive versatility have concerned groups where sexual potential is retained alongside a capacity for asexual propagation, either through vegetative reproduction or apomixis. Several examples where devices like bulbildery are concerned are discussed by Gustafsson (1947), as well as other cases, such as that described by Crane and Thomas (1940) for *Rubus*, where versatility lies in the capacity to form either reduced, sexually functional, or unreduced, apomictic, embryo sacs by the same plant. These instances relate to the simultaneous manifestation of two quite different kinds of reproduction, one permitting some level of recombination, the other excluding it entirely. Where reproduction is exclusively sexual, another form of versatility may be encountered, since many plants show a mixed breeding habit allowing both selfing and outcrossing. This

Reprinted by permission of the author and Society from *Transactions and Proceedings of the Botanical Society of Edinburgh* 40: 159–169, 1965–66.

may result from the inefficiency of an outbreeding mechanism, or from the operation of seemingly specific regulatory devices (Mather, 1943).

A striking feature of versatile reproductive systems in flowering plants is that they are often subject to control by environmental factors; where this is so, the genetic system itself may be said to exhibit phenotypic plasticity. Heretofore this fact has not been emphasised in discussions of the evolutionary importance of reproductive versatility. It is the purpose of this article to examine some of its implications, and in particular to consider whether environmentally-controlled variation in breeding behaviour has any special significance in the adaptive differentiation of flowering plant populations. As we currently understand this process, it depends upon the progressive accumulation of minor genetic changes under the pressure of natural selection. The genetic system plays a central role in determining the rate and nature of adaptive response, since it governs the generation, storage, release and recombination of genetic variation (Darlington, 1939). Components of the genetic system include the mechanical features of the chromosomes themselves which affect the rate of gene recombination; the breeding system, so far as it controls the degree of hybridity in a population; and the ecological properties of the species where these act to determine the size of breeding groups. In considering the role of the genetic system, Mather's concept of a compromise between "fitness" and "flexibility" (Mather, 1943) provides a valuable orienting principle. Fitness for an existing environment may mean failure in a future one; so evolutionary survival must frequently depend not only on producing genotypes adapted to current circumstances, but on the capacity to generate new ones to meet the altered circumstances of the morrow. Yet a genetic system fashioned to provide stability, and so short-term fitness, is likely to deprive a population of the flexibility required to permit continuous adaptive change over the longer term. Hence the compromise recognised by Mather. In each population a balance must exist between the factors making for a free release of variation and so for the potentiality of change, and those restraining the release of variation and so promoting fixity of type. Where this balance point will lie will depend upon the whole prior ecological history of the species, and numerous attributes of population and individual will be concerned. In general, however, some correlation is to be expected between the genetic system on the one hand, as the complex of factors determining the storage and flow of variation, and ecological habit and variation pattern on the other (Heslop-Harrison, 1964).

These correlations are not necessarily to be anticipated where selective factors impinging directly upon the reproductive system *per se* have favoured one or other type of breeding behaviour irrespective of the consequence in the long term for the flow of variability in the population. Thus it is noteworthy that the success of self-pollination systems is not always to be associated with their ultimate outcome, namely the establishment of virtually homozygous pure lines. Self-pollination may be favoured simply because the circumstances for cross-pollination do not exist, so that it offers the only means of producing progeny. Hagerup (1951) has shown how in the flora of the Faeroes normally outcrossing species are habitually selfed, often through the mechanical agency of rain, where there is a paucity of pollen vectors and a generally unfavourable climate for pollen-dispersal. Correspondingly, the survival of colonists after long distance dispersal may depend upon a capacity for selfing, and as Baker (1955) has suggested this may lead to the establishment of populations with a self-pollinating habit at the extremes of a species range.

It is also evident that a capacity for switching from one pollination mode to another could be advantageous in some circumstances. Such versatility may be manifest in two ways: inbreeding and outbreeding may alternate in a regular manner over an annual cycle, or one behaviour pattern may be the norm, with the other as a sporadically occurring alternative.

In the temperate flora several species are known to vary in their breeding behaviour throughout the year, and the phenomenon is particularly conspicuous when cleistogamous flowers are formed during the self-pollinating phase (Uphof, 1938). Perhaps the most celebrated examples of seasonally alternating cleistogamy and chasmogamy occur in the genus *Viola*, where there has been enough experimental study of the basis of control to show that temperature and photoperiod are principally concerned. Allard and Garner (1924) showed that short days promote cleistogamy and long days chasmogamy in *Viola fimbriatula* and *V. papilionacea*, and Chouard (1948) observed similar responses in *V. hirta* and *V. odorata*. In *V. sylvestris*, according to Chouard, flowering depends upon prior vernalisation; under short days a burst of chasmogamy ensues, but again cleistogamy is the rule during growth under long days. Evans (1956) found that *V. palustris* behaved in effectively the same manner. The conclusion is inescapable that many violet species have as a perfectly normal and regular feature of their reproductive behaviour a pattern of response to the major "time-keeping" environmental factors, temperature and photoperiod, which determines that they will be chasmogamous during the short days of spring and cleistogamous under the lengthening days of summer.

There is experimental evidence from other species, notably grasses of the tribe Andropogoneae, indicating a converse response. In some races of *Bothriochloa decipiens*, cleistogamous inflorescences form in short days, while chasmogamy is the rule under long days (Heslop-Harrison, 1961), and the same response has been observed in other related species. In *Rottboellia exaltata*, premature exposure to short-day inductive conditions reduces pollen fertility, and similarly promotes self-pollination (Heslop-Harrison, 1959). There is no field evidence to permit generalisation for these grass species, but the indication is that under natural conditions cleistogamy would prevail during the early flowering period, giving way to later chasmogamy.

These shifts in breeding behaviour co-ordinated with regularly varying environmental factors bear all the marks of adaptive responses, but the special advantage incurred is not immediately obvious, at least so far as the over-all effect on the genetic system is concerned. If the outcome is simply to establish that a proportion of the seed produced each year be the product of selfing, then the situation seems to differ in no essential respect from that arising when a proportion of flowers is selfed in a synchronously flowering, chasmogamous population. The effect of this kind of breeding behaviour is to reduce the average level of heterozygosity in the population as a whole, and so to slow down the flux of variability, while still preserving the capacity for response to selection over the long term (Mather, 1943). The seasonally varying breeding habit could thus be looked upon as a device permitting what Mather has termed a "controlled compromise" between inbreeding and out-breeding.

Perhaps, however, it is unjustified to argue that the adaptive value of seasonally regulated selfing lies in its effects on the genetic system at all. Rather might the property be one donating advantage in terms of repro-ductive potential under circumstances limiting cross-pollination, as in Hag-erup's Faeroese plants. It is significant that the cleistogamous violets are plants of shady habitats, and that their chasmogamous phase is early in the year, when the tree canopy is unformed and the possibility of insect visitation better. The later production of cleistogamous flowers under the deeper shade of summer may be the insurance against pollination failure. Obviously little can be said about seasonally-varying autogamy in the grasses of the Andro-pogoneae mentioned above without more knowledge of their general ecology, but it is noteworthy that the species showing a tendency to cleistogamy during the early part of a flowering period are short-lived, opportunistic plants of climates with hot dry summers when fire is a constant hazard. The capacity for building up large seed-populations in the early season by selfing may conceivably have an advantage under these circumstances. Two situations could be envisaged as promoting a trend towards homozygosity and so towards a break-up into local races. Should populations rarely reach a chas-mogamous phase through the curtailment—catastrophic or otherwise—of the growing season, the balance would be moved towards inbreeding. The same would be true should inbred progeny stand at so great a selective advan-tage in a particular prevailing environment that they came to constitute the greater proportion of the reproducing population each season.

The advantages usually attributed to the autogamous habit are, of course, associated with the trend to homozygosity. In a persistent phase of self-pollination, a population passes towards a state where the genetic variation is distributed among such pure lines as are adapted to survive in the con-ditions prevailing. In that these pure lines will unfailingly reproduce their like, the basis is offered for the build-up of large populations of a high average level of fitness. As Stebbins (1950, 1957) has stressed, this property could be of considerable value to colonists of temporary habitats—plants, that is to say, of weedy tendencies. For a species of this habit long-term survival in a changing environment will nevertheless demand also the retention of sufficient capacity for outbreeding to allow occasional recombination and release of variability. This could be achieved by sporadic outbreeding episodes, giving the condition termed cyclical autogamy by Fryxell (1959).

It has been emphasised elsewhere (Heslop-Harrison, 1964) that cyclical autogamy in Fryxell's sense must always be based upon response to varying environment. If, having retained a self-pollinating habit over a period of several generations, a lineage passes into a phase of cross-pollination, the cause can only be that it has encountered an unusual environmental circumstance, since the consequence of the previous inbreeding history will have been to stabilise the genetic basis of the breeding system along with all other genetic properties. The new circumstance could be a short-term fluctuation in the weather, a more profound climatic change, the experience of a new complex of environmental factors on migration into another locality, or even simply the appearance of pollinating agents.

This kind of "environmental control" of the breeding system may be contrasted with that involving a regular seasonal alternation, as in *Viola*. As we have seen, where the alternation is regular, the effect is to lower the average level of heterozygosity, but not necessarily to generate pure lines. Where reversion to outbreeding is no more than occasional the tendency will be towards a higher and higher degree of homozygosity in the inbreeding lineages, until an outbreeding event brings about a fresh burst of variation. It might be thought a singularly fortunate circumstance that selfing populations, parsimonious in their release of variation and in consequence illequipped to adapt to changing environments, should be caused to outbreed and so release variation by the very fact of environmental change. It is tempting, indeed, to suppose that where this is true the circumstance is not fortuitous, but that phenotypic plasticity in the breeding system is here itself an adaptive feature that has been moulded under selection.

In the absence of better experimental evidence this conclusion is perhaps presumptous, but the possibility is worth consideration. Inbreeding must certainly in all cases have evolved from outbreeding, and in many habitually inbreeding plants the derivation has meant little more than quite minor shifts of timing or in relative degrees of development of floral parts. Since floral ontogeny is affected by environmental factors, albeit to a lesser extent than vegetative growth, it is not surprising that environment-dependent variability should persist in the operation of inbreeding devices sufficient to bring about their occasional break-down and so a reversion to the ancestral breeding mode. Such a bonus would obviously not be thrown away by natural selection.

Autogamy is effective in establishing genetic uniformity only to the extent that it ultimately leads to homozygosity. Apomixis not only offers the possibility of a more rapid build up of uniform populations, but permits the fixation of heterozygous states. As with autogamy, obligate apomixis involves a sacrifice of evolutionary flexibility for immediate fitness. Again, versatility in reproductive method offers something of a compromise, and recognition of this has led to a shift away from the early view (expressed, for example, by Darlington, 1939) that apomixis represents no more than an evolutionary blind alley. The great diversification and high degree of ecological success that has been achieved by facultatively apomictic groups in genera like *Crataegus*, *Poa* and *Rubus* is evidence in itself that the capacity to replicate successful genotypes indefinitely while retaining the potential for producing new ones can be a substantial asset. The combination has been compared to the reproductive system in lower plants, where dispersal by condidia or other asexual spores ensures the distribution of successful genotypes generated by sexual processes (Heslop-Harrison, 1959a), and the same formula has been stabilised in the aphidids and other animal groups where sexual and agamic phases alternate.

Although it has been argued that the resort to apomixis must so retard evolutionary progress that apomictic lineages can never be expected to evolve beyond a species level, this viewpoint is appearing less secure as knowledge of the scale of incidence of apomictic tendencies in the flowering plant grows. The survey by Brown and Emery (1958) of apomixis in the panicoid grasses is illuminating. Apospory of much the same type is present in 28 % of the species of Panicoideae studied, and the apomictic forms are distributed among 22 genera. It seems almost certain that throughout its evolutionary history the tribe has preserved an apomictic tendency, alongside the sexual capacity necessary to permit diversification both at species and genus level.

The matter of environmental influence on reproductive versatility is again of some interest in facultatively apomictic groups. The prediction that the balance between sexuality and apomixis should be sensitive to external control (Heslop-Harrison, 1959a) has been proven justified in one experimentally-studied species, again a grass of the Andropogoneae, *Dichanthium aristatum* (Knox and Heslop-Harrison, 1963). Under phytotron conditions, the proportion of aposporous embryo sacs produced by plants of an Australian race of this species could be caused to vary within wide limits through the agency of the light regime. In the last two or three years Dr. R. B. Knox has been conducting surveys of the relative incidence of apomixis and sexuality in natural populations of this grass in Australia. He has recently reported to the Brisbane Plant Breeding Conference evidence showing unequivocally that in some populations in the field practically all reproduction in the early part of the flowering season in daylengths under 12 hours is apomictic, while in the later phase, under long days, the proportion of apomictic embryo sacs falls to less than 50 %.

Should the system now confirmed both in experimental and field conditions in *Dichanthium artistatum* be in any sense characteristic of apospory in the Panicoideae, then it is indeed evident that this important group of grasses has evolved a reproductive system comparable with that of the aphidids and lower plant groups with alternating sexual and asexual reproductive phases. As with these groups the opportunity is open for the total abandonment of sexuality in the interests of extreme ecological specialisation—the imperfect fungi offer a model—or for the reclamation of sexuality when circumstances require. There would seem to be no barriers to evolutionary diversification at any level with such a genetic system.

Environmentally-modulated reproductive systems have been referred to above as revealing phenotypic plasticity. With the examples reviewed above in mind, it seems justifiable to conclude that such plasticity could be of adaptive significance in those groups whose ecological habit demands the rapid build-up of uniformly well adapted populations when suitable habitats are available, coupled with the ability to produce genotypes to meet new demands resulting from either habitat change or migration. The special value of sensitivity to environmental controls would seem to lie in the facility it gives for matching reproductive method to time of year in the same way that flower initiation itself is related to season in photoperiodically sensitive species. Evidently such a facility will offer different possibilities from those offered by a versatile reproductive system giving a fixed ratio of the different behaviour patterns at all times; but how exactly this is likely to affect the success of any particular race or species can only be understood in relation to its general ecology, and especially the kinds of community to which it belongs.

●　●　●

References

Allard, H. A., and W. W. Garner. (1946). *United States Dept. of Agriculture Technical Bulletin* No. **727**.

Baker, H. G. (1953). Race formation and reproductive method in flowering plants. *Symp. Soc. Exp. Biol.* No. 7.

—— (1955). Self-compatibility and establishment after long distance dispersal. *Evolution* **9**, 347–348.

—— (1959). Reproductive methods as factors in specification in flowering plants. *Cold Spring Harb. Symp. Quant. Biol.* **24**, 177–199.

Brown, W. V., and W. H. P. Emery. (1958). Apomixis in the Gramineae: Panicoideae. *Amer. J. Bot.* **45**, 253–263.

Chouard, P. (1948). Diversité de type de compartement au photo- et au thermopériodisme dans le genre *Viola* (Violettes et Pensées). *C. R. Acad. Sci. Paris* **226**, 1831–1833.

Crane, M. B., and P. T. Thomas. (1940). Reproductive versatility in *Rubus. J. Genet.*, **40**, 109–128.

Darlington, C. D. (1939). *The Evolution of Genetic Systems*. 1st Ed. Cambridge University Press.

Evans, L. T. (1956). Chasmogamous flowering in *Viola palustris*. *Nature Lond.* **178**, 1301.

Fryxell, P. A. (1959). The evolutionary position of inbreeding systems. *Advances in Botany, Vol.* **1**, 887–891. Toronto University Press.

Grant, V. (1958). The regulation of recombination in plants. *Cold Spring Harb. Symp. Quant. Biol.* **23**, 337–363.

Gustafsson, A. (1947). Apomixis in higher plants. *Acta Univ. Lund. N. F. Avd. 2* **42-43**, 1–307.

Hagerup, O. (1951). Pollination in the Faroes—in spite of rain and the poverty of insects. *Kgl. Dansk Vid. Selsk. Biol. Meddel.* **18**, 3–48.

Heslop-Harrison, J. (1959a). Apomixis, environment and adaptation. *Advances in Botany, Vol.* **1**, 891–895. Toronto University Press.

———. (1959b). Photoperiod and fertility in *Rottoboellia exaltata* L. f. *Ann. Bot. N. S.* **22**, 345–349.

———. (1961). The function of the glume pit and the control of cleistogamy in *Bothriochloa decipiens*. *Phytomorph.* **11**, 378–383.

———. (1964). Forty years of genecology. In *Advances in Ecological Research, Vol.* **2**, Ed. J. B. Cragg, 159–247. Academic Press.

Knox, R. B., and J. Heslop-Harrison. (1963). Experimental control of aposporous apomixis in a grass of the Andropogoneae. *Bot. Not.* **116**, 127–141.

Mather, K. (1943). Polygenic inheritance and natural selection. *Biol. Rev.* **18**, 32–64.

Stebbins, G. L. (1950). *Variation and Evolution in Plants*. Columbia University Press.

———. (1957). Self-fertilisation and population variability in the higher plants. *Amer. Nat.* **91**, 337–354.

———. (1958). Longevity, habitat and release of genetic variability in the higher plants. *Cold Spring Harb. Symp. Quant. Biol.* **23**, 365–378.

Uphof, J. C. T. (1938). Cleistogamic flowers. *Bot. Rev.* **4**, 21–49.

Index